WHSmith

Practice

Maths

Steve Mills and Hilary Koll

Contents

Age 12–14
Years 8–9
Key Stage 3

Introduction

Maths Practice

Practice Key Maths Skills is for anyone who is struggling to understand concepts in percentages and algebra. These topics can be difficult at first, but this simple, step-by-step approach should have you mastering tricky ideas in no time.

Pages 3–14 of this book are all about understanding percentages, estimating and calculating them and converting them to fractions and decimals. Pages 15–26 deal with percentage change including finding percentage increases and decreases in real-life problems. Also covered is writing an amount as a percentage of another amount. and decimals and equivalence. Pages 27–38 deal equations and formulae, including solving equations using two different methods (you can choose the method you prefer). Also covered are formulae and changing the subject of them.

How to use *Maths Practice*

Work through each section in order, reading all the clues and tips as you go through the exercises. You will need to cut out the cards in the book to use for some activities. Make sure you keep these cards in a safe place, such as an envelope, so you can re-use them.

When you feel confident with what is written on a particular page, turn over and try to answer the questions on the next page. Carefully mark all your answers to see how you got on. If you still have any difficulties and feel you need some more practice, try some of the activities again or re-read the tips and comments. If you feel confident and have got most of the questions right, move on to the next section.

You might find it helpful to make a list of all the key words that you come across in this book and write down the meanings. This will help you try to answer the questions.

Hachette UK's policy is to use papers that are natural, renewable and recyclable products and made from wood grown in sustainable forests. The logging and manufacturing processes are expected to conform to the environmental regulations of the country of origin.

Orders: please contact Bookpoint Ltd, 130 Milton Park, Abingdon, Oxon OX14 4SB.
Telephone: (44) 01235 827720. Fax: (44) 01235 400454. Lines are open 9.00a.m.–5.00p.m., Monday to Saturday, with a 24-hour message answering service. Visit our website at www.hoddereducation.co.uk.

First published in 2007 exclusively for WHSmith by
Hodder Education
An Hachette UK Company
338 Euston Road
London NW1 3BH

This second edition first published in 2013 exclusively for WHSmith by Hodder Education.

Impression number 10 9 8 7 6 5 4 3 2
Year 2018 2017 2016 2015 2014 2013

Cover illustration by Oxford Designers and Illustrators Ltd
All other illustrations by Fakenham Prepress Solutions, Fakenham, Norfolk NR21 8NN
Typeset in 16pt Folio by Fakenham Prepress Solutions, Fakenham, Norfolk NR21 8NN
Printed in Italy

A catalogue record for this title is available from the British Library.

ISBN: 978 1444 189 308

Estimating percentages

Practice

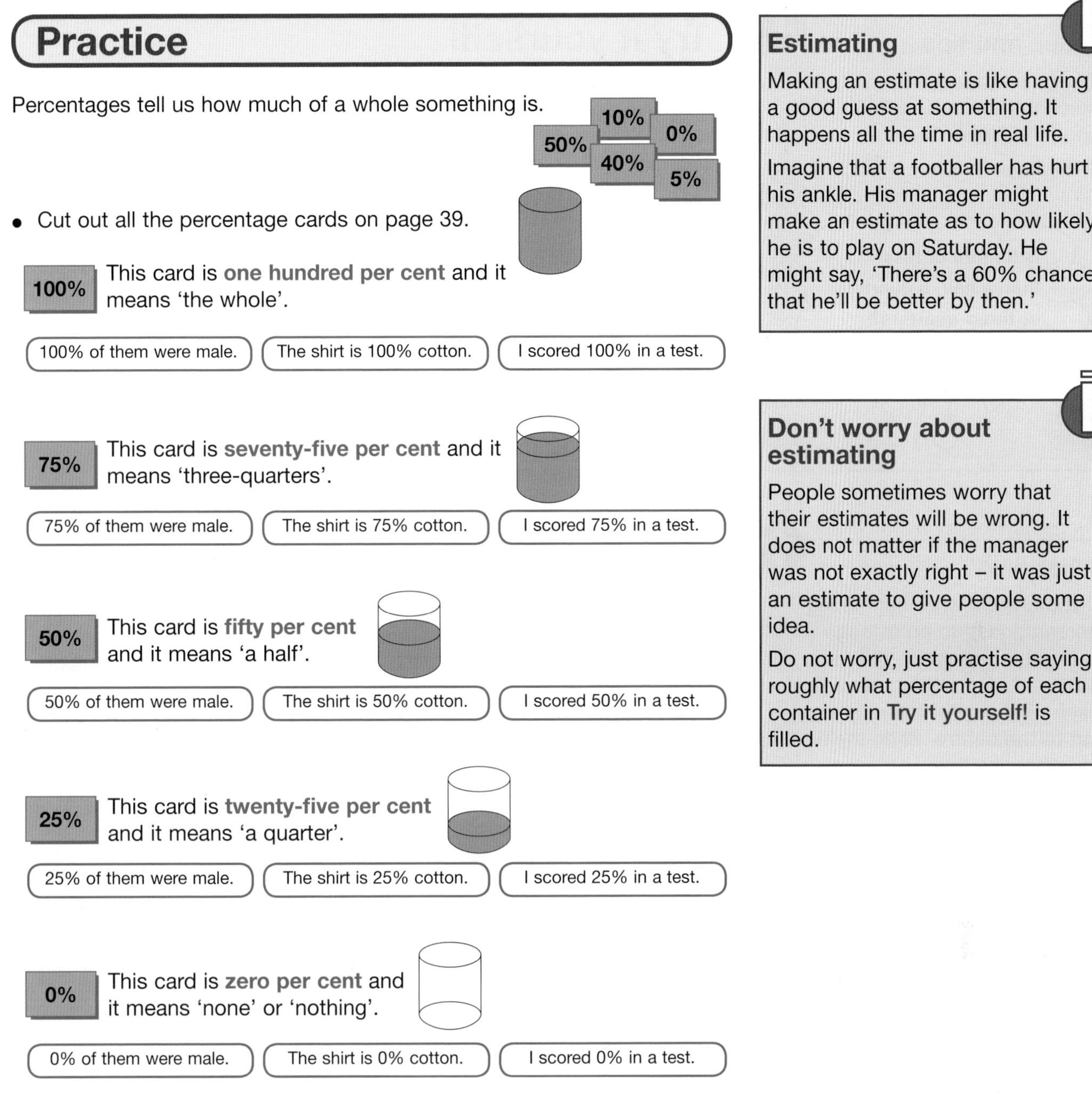

Percentages tell us how much of a whole something is.

- Cut out all the percentage cards on page 39.

100% This card is **one hundred per cent** and it means 'the whole'.

100% of them were male. | The shirt is 100% cotton. | I scored 100% in a test.

75% This card is **seventy-five per cent** and it means 'three-quarters'.

75% of them were male. | The shirt is 75% cotton. | I scored 75% in a test.

50% This card is **fifty per cent** and it means 'a half'.

50% of them were male. | The shirt is 50% cotton. | I scored 50% in a test.

25% This card is **twenty-five per cent** and it means 'a quarter'.

25% of them were male. | The shirt is 25% cotton. | I scored 25% in a test.

0% This card is **zero per cent** and it means 'none' or 'nothing'.

0% of them were male. | The shirt is 0% cotton. | I scored 0% in a test.

Try it yourself!

Estimate what percentage of each container is filled and find a card showing that percentage.

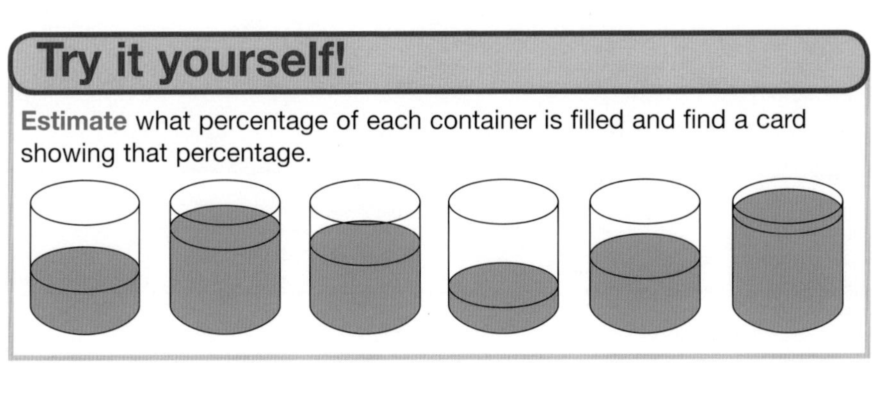

Estimating

Making an estimate is like having a good guess at something. It happens all the time in real life.

Imagine that a footballer has hurt his ankle. His manager might make an estimate as to how likely he is to play on Saturday. He might say, 'There's a 60% chance that he'll be better by then.'

Don't worry about estimating

People sometimes worry that their estimates will be wrong. It does not matter if the manager was not exactly right – it was just an estimate to give people some idea.

Do not worry, just practise saying roughly what percentage of each container in **Try it yourself!** is filled.

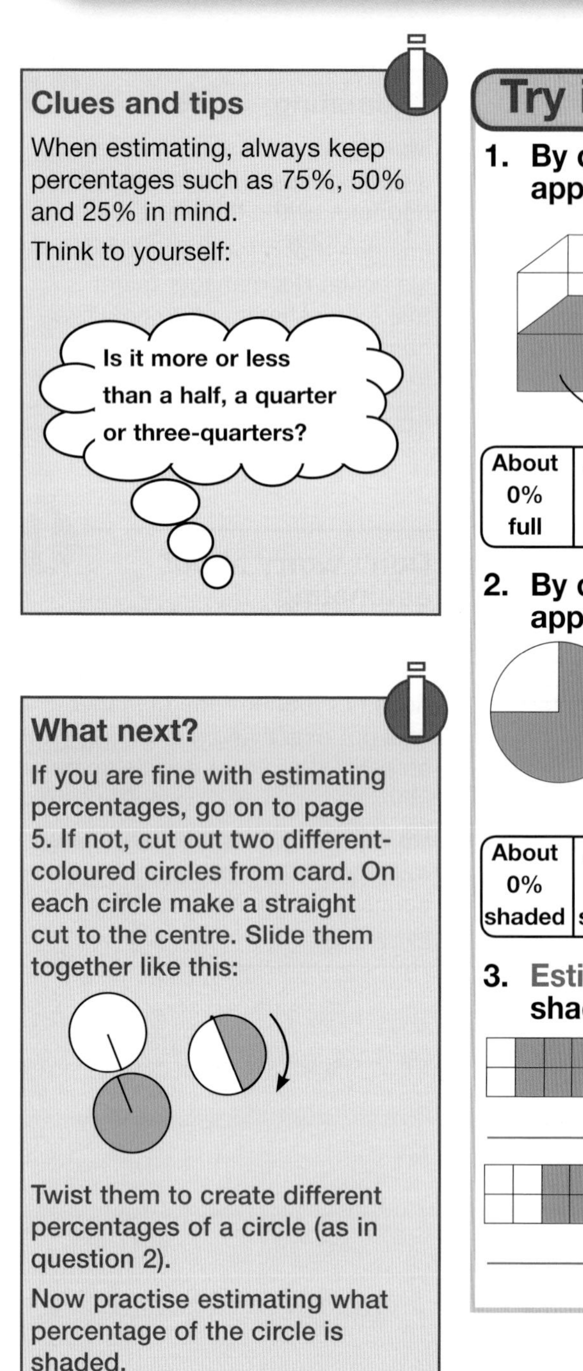

Clues and tips

When estimating, always keep percentages such as 75%, 50% and 25% in mind.

Think to yourself:

What next?

If you are fine with estimating percentages, go on to page 5. If not, cut out two different-coloured circles from card. On each circle make a straight cut to the centre. Slide them together like this:

Twist them to create different percentages of a circle (as in question 2).

Now practise estimating what percentage of the circle is shaded.

Try it yourself!

1. By drawing lines, match each container with an appropriate estimate.

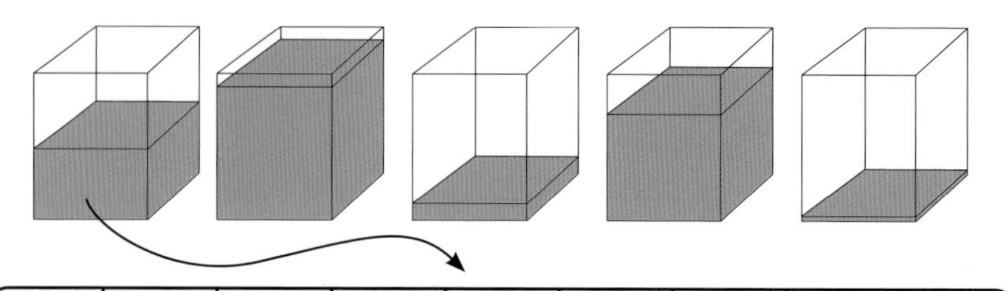

About 0% full	About 5% full	About 10% full	About 20% full	About 50% full	About 65% full	About 75% full	About 95% full	About 100% full

2. By drawing lines, match each shape with an appropriate estimate.

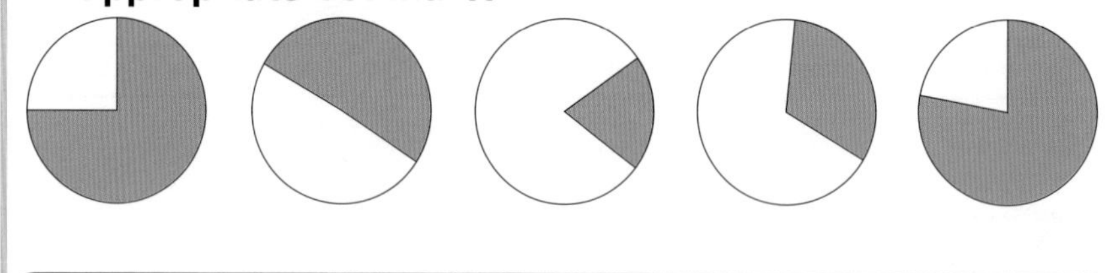

About 0% shaded	About 10% shaded	About 20% shaded	About 35% shaded	About 50% shaded	About 65% shaded	About 75% shaded	About 80% shaded	About 100% shaded

3. Estimate roughly what percentage of each shape is shaded.

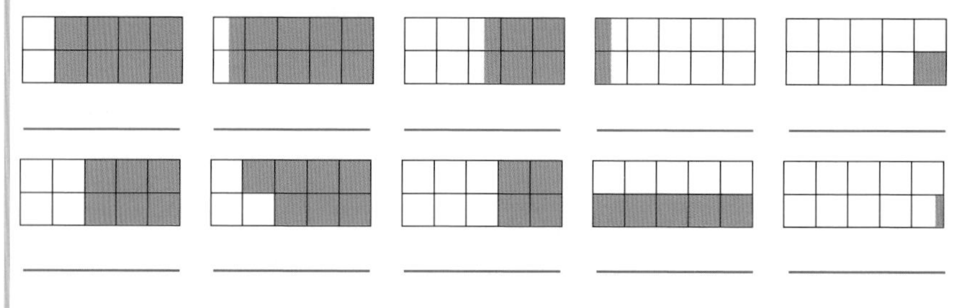

Teacher's tips

A good way to practice estimating is to eliminate what it **isn't**. Start at the extremes – is it zero, 100%? Which is it closest to? Repeat with 50%, 25%, 10% and so on until you get a more accurate estimate.

Out of 100

Practice

- Instead of having to guess a percentage, it helps if the shape or container shows 100 equal parts.

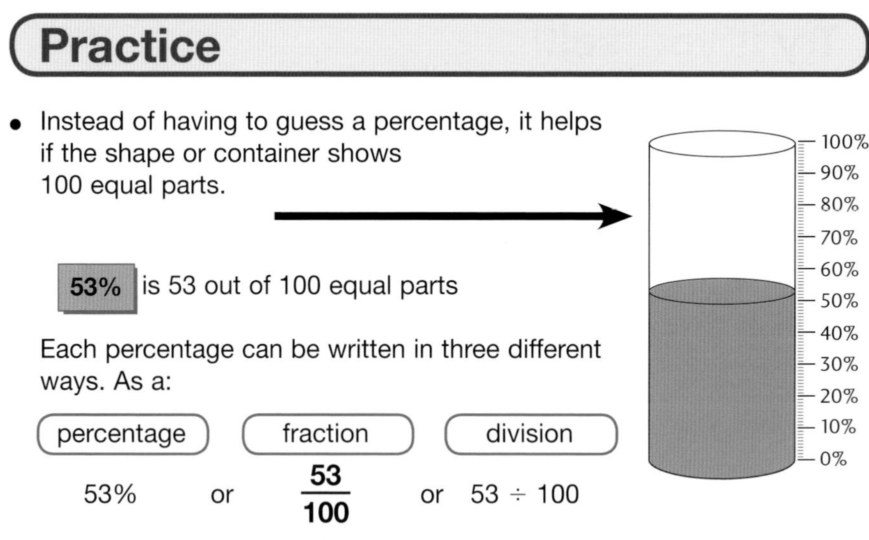

53% is 53 out of 100 equal parts

Each percentage can be written in three different ways. As a:

percentage		fraction		division
53%	or	$\frac{53}{100}$	or	53 ÷ 100

- Some percentages can be written as **fractions** in *more than one* way. Write each of these as a fraction (out of 100).

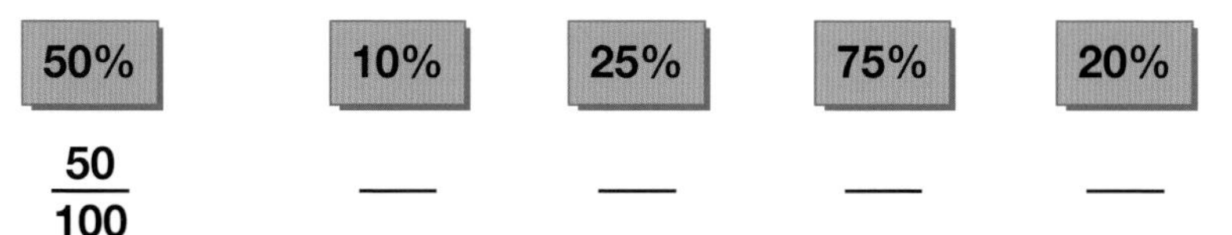

50%	10%	25%	75%	20%
$\frac{50}{100}$	___	___	___	___

- Notice that each fraction can be changed to its **simplest form** by dividing the top and bottom numbers by the same number. Change each fraction above to its simplest form by dividing.

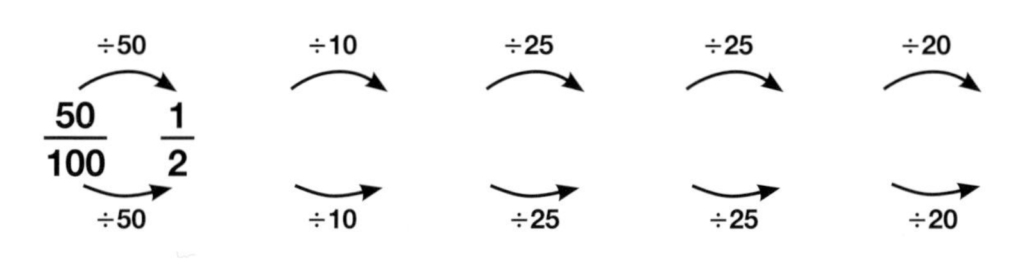

÷50	÷10	÷25	÷25	÷20
$\frac{50}{100} \rightarrow \frac{1}{2}$				
÷50	÷10	÷25	÷25	÷20

- So, 50% can be written as $\frac{50}{100}$ or $\frac{1}{2}$.

Try it yourself!

Pick a percentage card and describe it:

- as a **fraction** (out of 100)
- and as a **division question** (divided by 100).

Do this several times to get the hang of it.

Always think of the % sign as 'out of 100' or 'divided by 100'.

Why percentages?

Percentages are used in everyday life in all sorts of different ways. Look out for these ways, such as:

- Sale 50% off
- Bloggs Bank offers 5% interest on savings
- Smith: only 60% chance of playing in match

Word wise

Per cent means 'out of 100'. **Per** means 'out of' and **cent** is 100, as in words like *centimetre*, *century*.

Simplest form

A **fraction** can be changed to its **simplest form** by dividing the top number (the numerator) and bottom number (the denominator) by the same number.

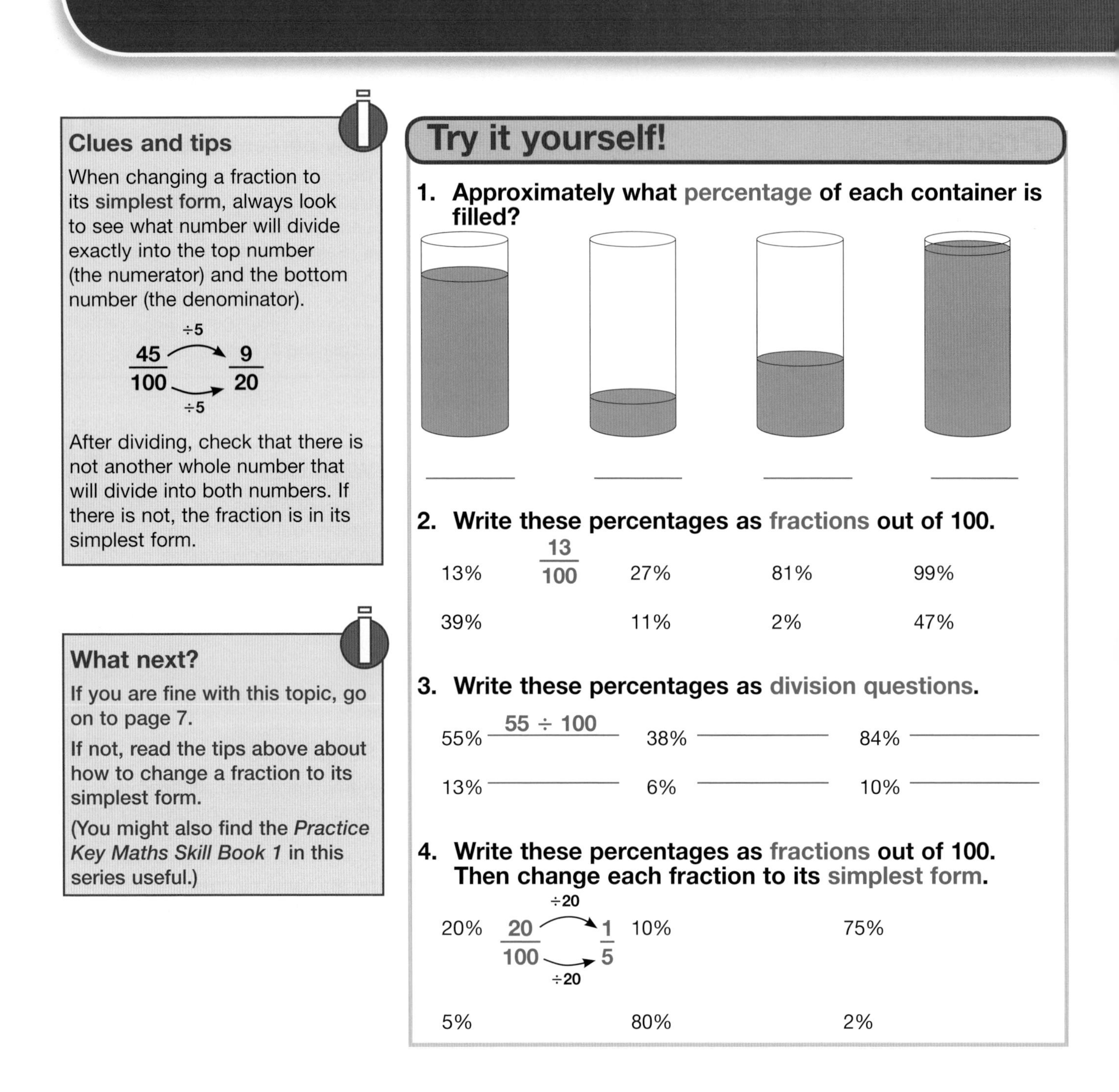

Clues and tips

When changing a fraction to its simplest form, always look to see what number will divide exactly into the top number (the numerator) and the bottom number (the denominator).

$$\frac{45}{100} \xrightarrow{\div 5} \frac{9}{20}$$

After dividing, check that there is not another whole number that will divide into both numbers. If there is not, the fraction is in its simplest form.

What next?

If you are fine with this topic, go on to page 7.

If not, read the tips above about how to change a fraction to its simplest form.

(You might also find the *Practice Key Maths Skill Book 1* in this series useful.)

Try it yourself!

1. Approximately what percentage of each container is filled?

______ ______ ______ ______

2. Write these percentages as fractions out of 100.

13% $\frac{13}{100}$	27%	81%	99%
39%	11%	2%	47%

3. Write these percentages as division questions.

55% 55 ÷ 100	38% ______	84% ______
13% ______	6% ______	10% ______

4. Write these percentages as fractions out of 100. Then change each fraction to its simplest form.

20% $\frac{20}{100} \xrightarrow{\div 20} \frac{1}{5}$	10%	75%
5%	80%	2%

Teacher's tips

Calculate percentages when you're shopping to see how much a saving on a sale item is, or if a discount is actually worth having. Look out for clever ways some shops make some deals seem better than they really are!

Percentages, fractions and decimals

Practice

- Percentages, fractions and decimals are like three different languages. They are just different ways of describing the same thing.

- Remember that percentages can be written as **fractions** and that some percentages can be written as *more than one* fraction, for example:

  50% can be written as $\frac{50}{100}$ or $\frac{1}{2}$

- Percentages can also be written as **decimals**. It is easy if the percentage is written as a **division question**.
  24% is 24 ÷ 100
  24 ÷ 100 = 0.24

Work this division question out in your head or using a calculator to get a decimal answer.

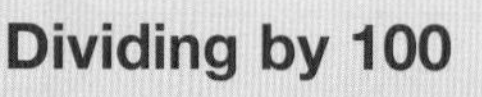

Try it yourself!

Pick a percentage card and write it as a **division question**.

Then work out the answer as a **decimal** in your head or using a calculator.

42% 42 ÷ 100 = 0.42

Look for a pattern as to what happens when you divide a number by 100. You will soon discover how easy it is.

Remember these rules:

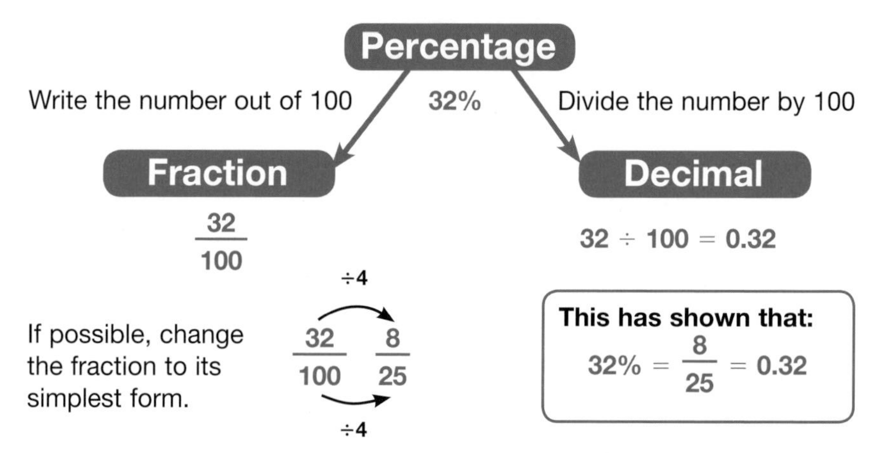

This has shown that:
$32\% = \frac{8}{25} = 0.32$

Percentages, fractions and decimals

Percentages, fractions and decimals are all used to describe what part of a whole something is.

If someone asked what proportion of a class was girls, the answer could be given
as a fraction, e.g. $\frac{1}{2}$,
as a percentage, e.g. 50%,
or as a decimal, e.g. 0.5.

Dividing by 100

It is easy to divide by 100 in your head.

Just move the digits of the number two places to the right. The decimal point remains in the same place.

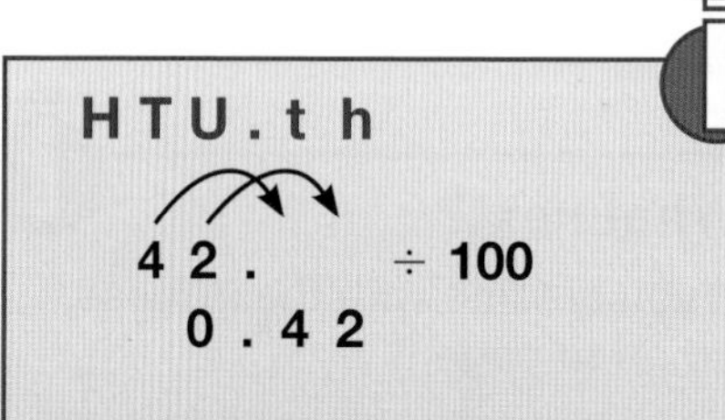

Notice that we write 0.42 rather than .42 as it is easy to miss the decimal point otherwise.

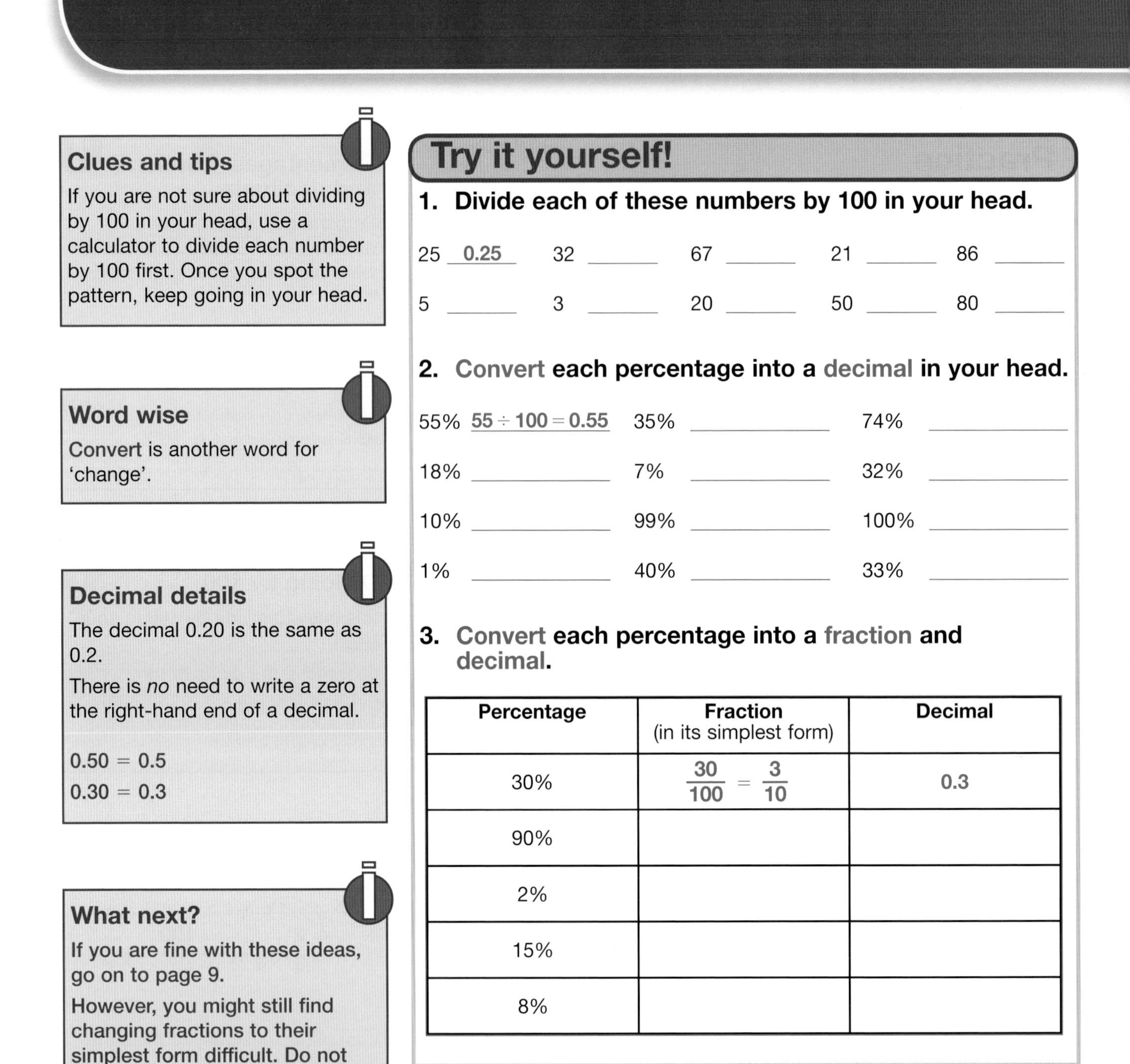

Clues and tips

If you are not sure about dividing by 100 in your head, use a calculator to divide each number by 100 first. Once you spot the pattern, keep going in your head.

Word wise

Convert is another word for 'change'.

Decimal details

The decimal 0.20 is the same as 0.2.

There is *no* need to write a zero at the right-hand end of a decimal.

0.50 = 0.5
0.30 = 0.3

What next?

If you are fine with these ideas, go on to page 9.

However, you might still find changing fractions to their simplest form difficult. Do not worry. As long as you can write them as fractions out of 100 at the moment, you will be okay to move on to page 9.

If you feel you still need more practice, use your percentage cards.

Try it yourself!

1. Divide each of these numbers by 100 in your head.

25 0.25 32 ______ 67 ______ 21 ______ 86 ______

5 ______ 3 ______ 20 ______ 50 ______ 80 ______

2. Convert each percentage into a decimal in your head.

55% 55 ÷ 100 = 0.55 35% ______ 74% ______

18% ______ 7% ______ 32% ______

10% ______ 99% ______ 100% ______

1% ______ 40% ______ 33% ______

3. Convert each percentage into a fraction and decimal.

Percentage	Fraction (in its simplest form)	Decimal
30%	$\frac{30}{100} = \frac{3}{10}$	0.3
90%		
2%		
15%		
8%		

Teacher's tips

Remember to use the percentage symbol (%) every time you are writing a percentage. Sometimes people misuse percentages in everyday life, so don't get caught out! Can a sportsman really try '150%' for instance?

Calculating percentages in your head

Practice

- There are many different ways to **calculate** a percentage of a number in your head.

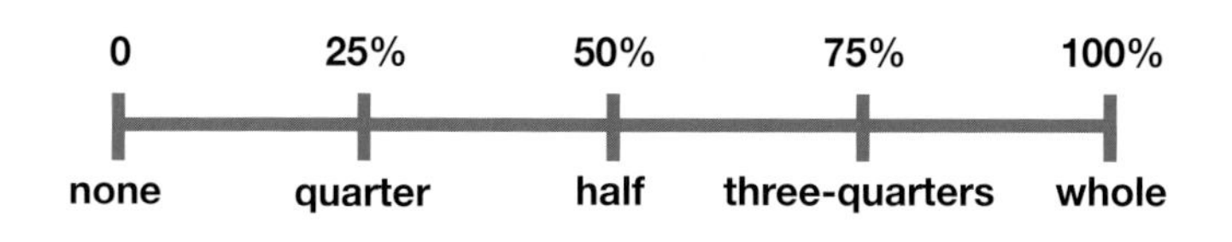

Remember first that 50% is $\frac{1}{2}$, 25% is $\frac{1}{4}$ and 75% is $\frac{3}{4}$.
Here are some of the ways:

- To calculate **50%**: halve the number.
  50% of £300 → **half** of £300 = £150
  50% of 820 g → **half** of 820 g = 410 g

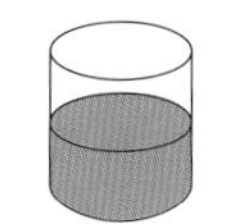

- To calculate **25%**: halve the number and halve the answer (or just divide by 4).
  25% of £300 → **half** of £300 = £150 → **half** of £150 = £75
  25% of 820 g → **half** of 820 g = 410 g → **half** of 410 g = 205 g

- To calculate **75%**: halve the number and halve the answer. Then add the two answers together.
  75% of £300 → **half** of £300 = £150 → **half** of £150 = £75
  → £150 + £75 = £225
  75% of 820 g → **half** of 820 g = 410 g → **half** of 410 g = 205 g
  → 410 g + 205 g = 615 g

Try it yourself!

You will need these three percentage cards from page 15. Also cut out the number cards on page 17.

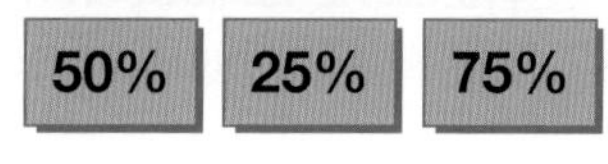

Pick a number card and a percentage card and **calculate** that percentage of the number in your head.

of **120** = 60

Do this as many times as you can until you get the hang of it.

Word wise

Calculate does *not* mean 'use a calculator'.

It means 'work out the answer'.

You can calculate in your head, on paper or using a calculator.

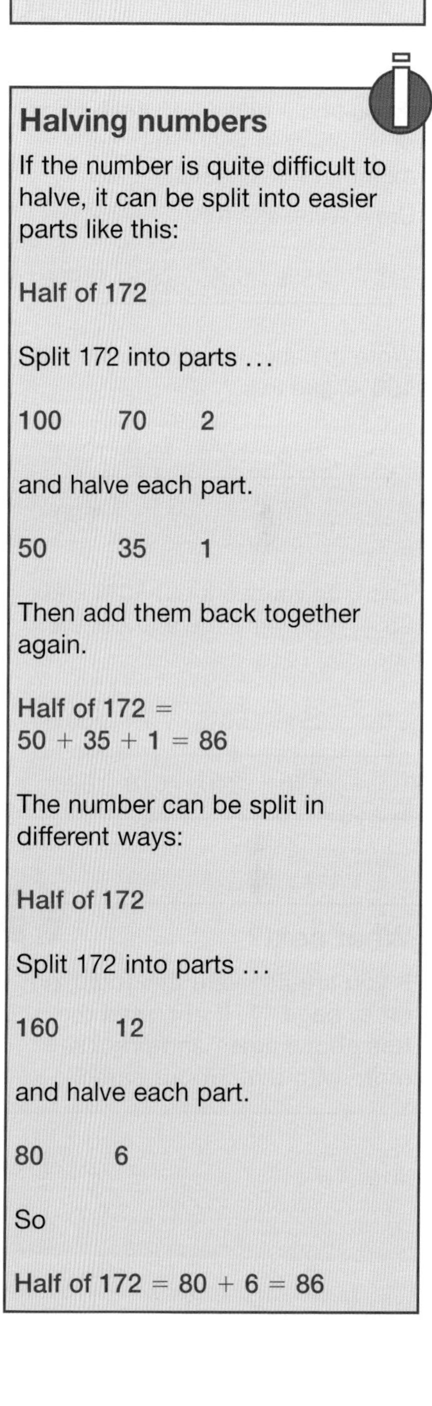

Halving numbers

If the number is quite difficult to halve, it can be split into easier parts like this:

Half of 172

Split 172 into parts …

100 70 2

and halve each part.

50 35 1

Then add them back together again.

Half of 172 =
50 + 35 + 1 = 86

The number can be split in different ways:

Half of 172

Split 172 into parts …

160 12

and halve each part.

80 6

So

Half of 172 = 80 + 6 = 86

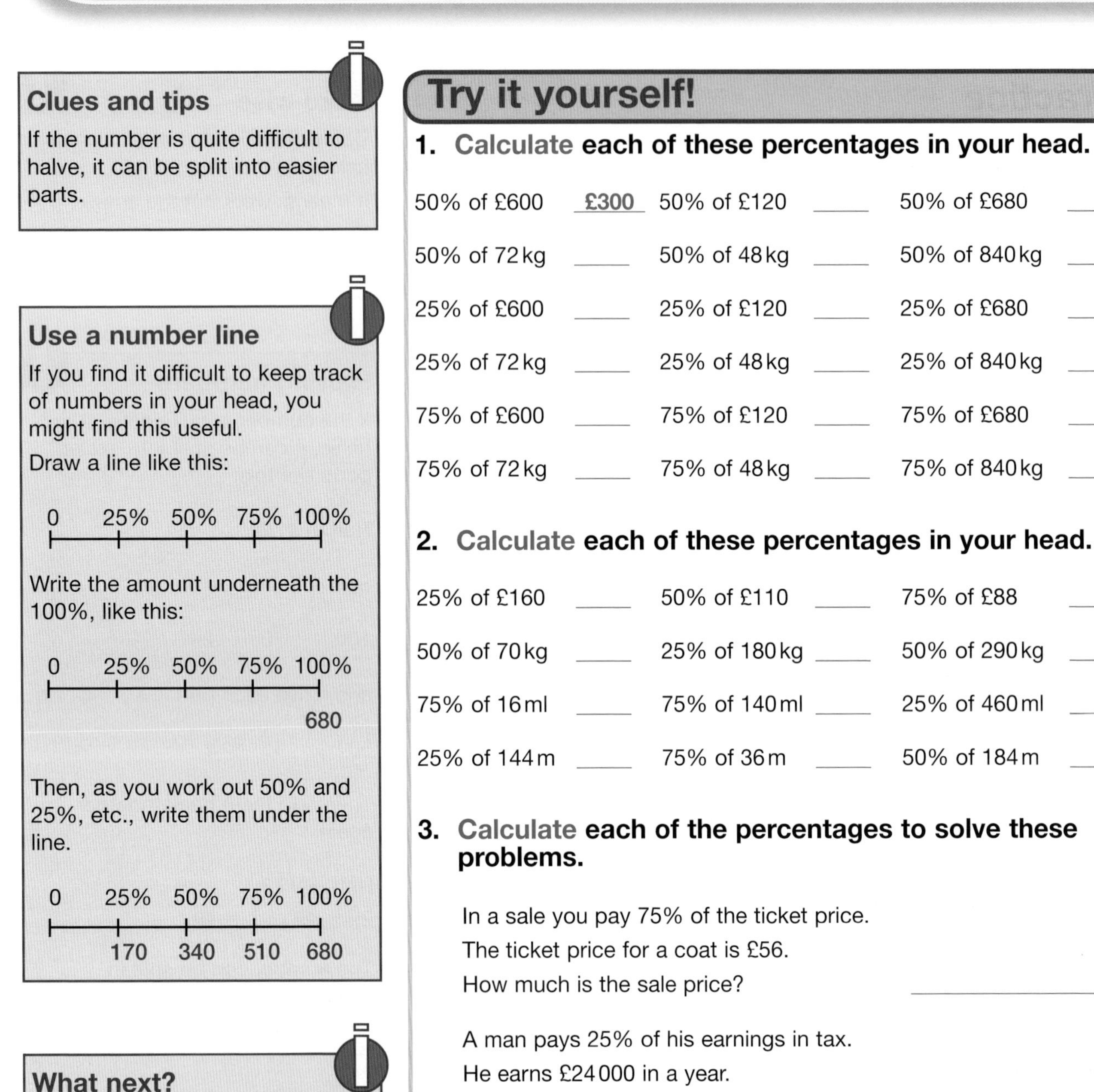

Clues and tips

If the number is quite difficult to halve, it can be split into easier parts.

Use a number line

If you find it difficult to keep track of numbers in your head, you might find this useful.

Draw a line like this:

0 25% 50% 75% 100%

Write the amount underneath the 100%, like this:

0 25% 50% 75% 100%

680

Then, as you work out 50% and 25%, etc., write them under the line.

0 25% 50% 75% 100%

170 340 510 680

What next?

If you are fine with this topic, go on to page 11. If not, read the tips above again and practise more with the cut-out cards.

Try it yourself!

1. Calculate each of these percentages in your head.

50% of £600	£300	50% of £120	____	50% of £680	____
50% of 72 kg	____	50% of 48 kg	____	50% of 840 kg	____
25% of £600	____	25% of £120	____	25% of £680	____
25% of 72 kg	____	25% of 48 kg	____	25% of 840 kg	____
75% of £600	____	75% of £120	____	75% of £680	____
75% of 72 kg	____	75% of 48 kg	____	75% of 840 kg	____

2. Calculate each of these percentages in your head.

25% of £160	____	50% of £110	____	75% of £88	____
50% of 70 kg	____	25% of 180 kg	____	50% of 290 kg	____
75% of 16 ml	____	75% of 140 ml	____	25% of 460 ml	____
25% of 144 m	____	75% of 36 m	____	50% of 184 m	____

3. Calculate each of the percentages to solve these problems.

In a sale you pay 75% of the ticket price.
The ticket price for a coat is £56.
How much is the sale price? ____________

A man pays 25% of his earnings in tax.
He earns £24 000 in a year.
How much tax does he pay? ____________

A mobile phone company has a 50% sale.
How much will a phone cost in the sale if it usually costs £78? ____________

Teacher's tips

It's easy to calculate 10% (by dividing the amount by 10), so one way to calculate a percentage mentally is break down the amount into lots of 10%. 20% is divide by 10 and then double, and so on.

Calculating other percentages

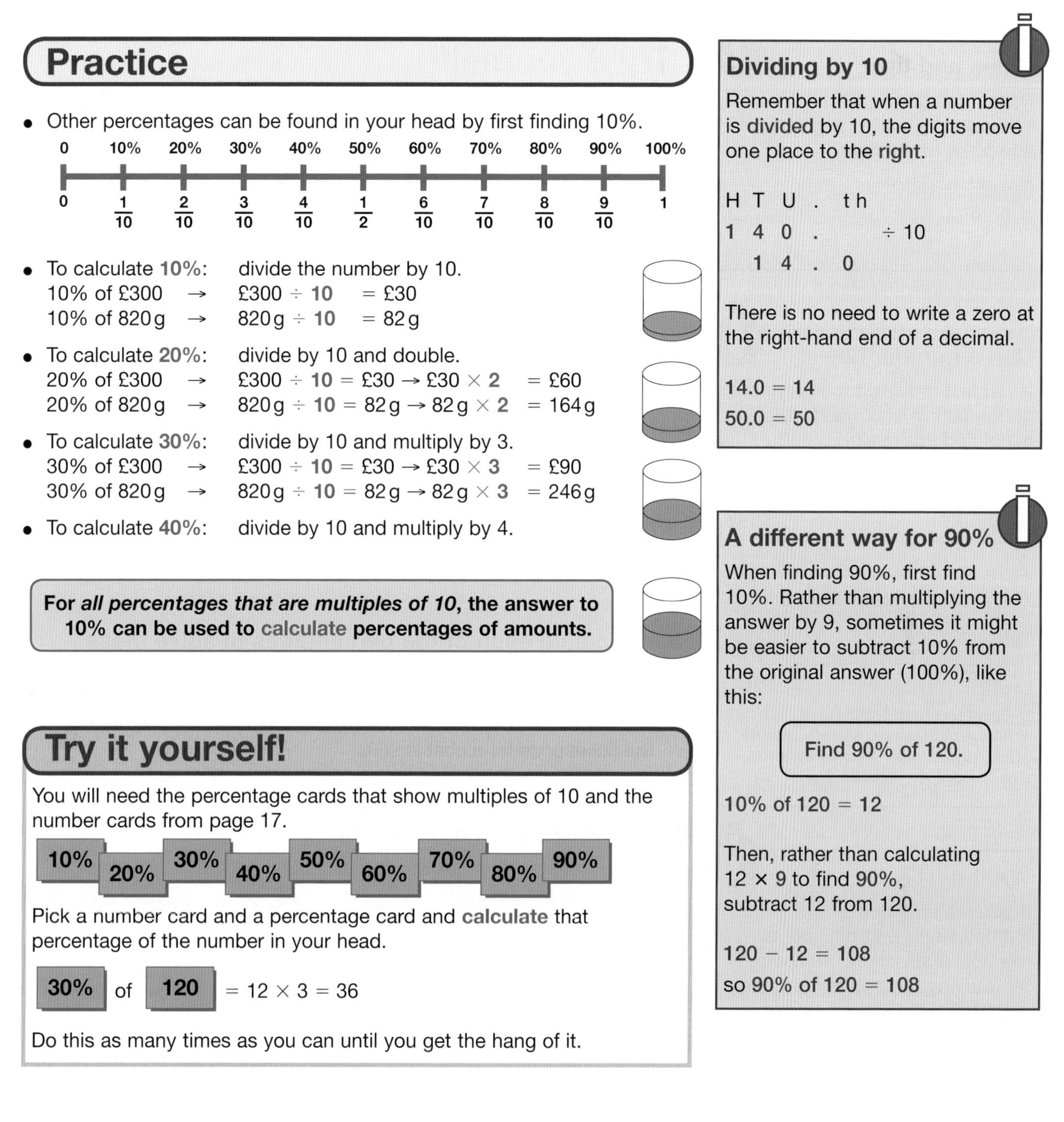

Practice

- Other percentages can be found in your head by first finding 10%.

- To calculate **10%**: divide the number by 10.
  10% of £300 → £300 ÷ **10** = £30
  10% of 820 g → 820 g ÷ **10** = 82 g
- To calculate **20%**: divide by 10 and double.
  20% of £300 → £300 ÷ **10** = £30 → £30 × **2** = £60
  20% of 820 g → 820 g ÷ **10** = 82 g → 82 g × **2** = 164 g
- To calculate **30%**: divide by 10 and multiply by 3.
  30% of £300 → £300 ÷ **10** = £30 → £30 × **3** = £90
  30% of 820 g → 820 g ÷ **10** = 82 g → 82 g × **3** = 246 g
- To calculate **40%**: divide by 10 and multiply by 4.

For *all percentages that are multiples of 10*, the answer to 10% can be used to calculate percentages of amounts.

Try it yourself!

You will need the percentage cards that show multiples of 10 and the number cards from page 17.

10% **20%** **30%** **40%** **50%** **60%** **70%** **80%** **90%**

Pick a number card and a percentage card and **calculate** that percentage of the number in your head.

30% of **120** = 12 × 3 = 36

Do this as many times as you can until you get the hang of it.

Dividing by 10

Remember that when a number is divided by 10, the digits move one place to the right.

H	T	U	.	th	
1	4	0	.		÷ 10
	1	4	.	0	

There is no need to write a zero at the right-hand end of a decimal.

14.0 = 14

50.0 = 50

A different way for 90%

When finding 90%, first find 10%. Rather than multiplying the answer by 9, sometimes it might be easier to subtract 10% from the original answer (100%), like this:

Find 90% of 120.

10% of 120 = 12

Then, rather than calculating 12 × 9 to find 90%, subtract 12 from 120.

120 − 12 = 108

so 90% of 120 = 108

Check that the answer is 'about right'.

30% is just a bit more than 25% or $\frac{1}{4}$.

$\frac{1}{4}$ of 120 = 30. **36 is a bit more than 30.**

So it is about right.

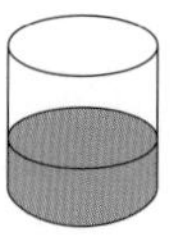

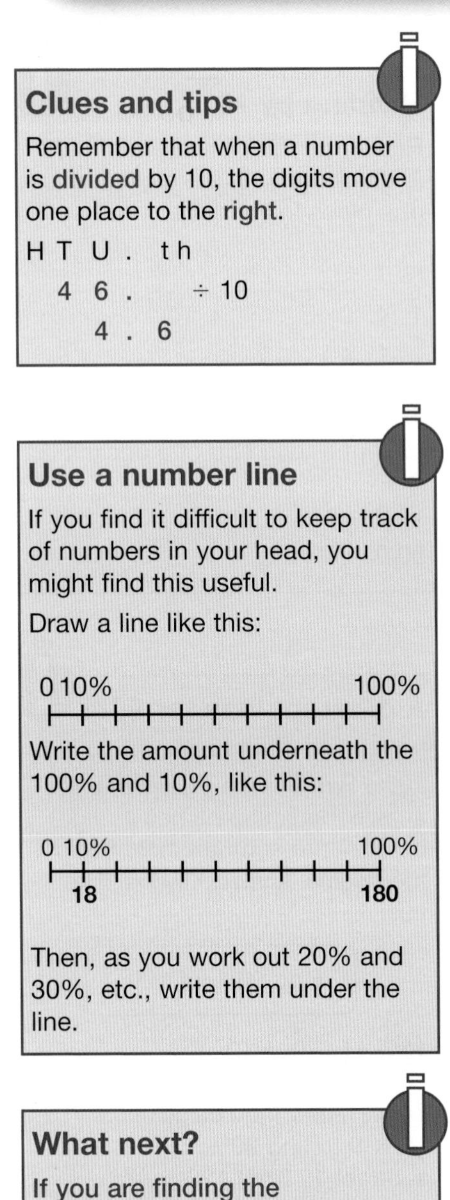

Clues and tips

Remember that when a number is divided by 10, the digits move one place to the right.

H	T	U	.	th	
	4	6	.		÷ 10
		4	.	6	

Use a number line

If you find it difficult to keep track of numbers in your head, you might find this useful.

Draw a line like this:

0 10% 100%

Write the amount underneath the 100% and 10%, like this:

0 10% 100%

18 180

Then, as you work out 20% and 30%, etc., write them under the line.

What next?

If you are finding the multiplication part difficult, re-read the instructions above and try drawing a number line to help you. Practise further with your cards if you need to.

Try it yourself!

1. Calculate each of these percentages in your head.

10% of £600	£60	10% of £120	______	10% of £680	______
10% of 72 kg	7.2 kg	10% of 48 kg	______	10% of 84 kg	______
20% of £600	______	20% of £120	______	20% of £680	______
20% of 72 kg	______	20% of 48 kg	______	20% of 84 kg	______

2. Calculate each of these percentages in your head.

30% of £60	______	60% of £40	______	80% of £90	______
40% of 70 kg	______	90% of 110 kg	______	20% of 35 kg	______
70% of 80 ml	______	40% of 120 ml	______	80% of 300 ml	______
90% of 140 m	______	70% of 110 km	______	30% of 184 m	______

3. Calculate each of the percentages to solve these problems.

In a sale you pay 80% of the ticket price.
The ticket price for a coat is £60.
How much is the sale price? ______

A woman pays 30% of her earnings in tax.
She earns £12 000 in a year.
How much tax does she pay? ______

A baby girl weighs 90% of her expected weight.
Her expected weight was 130 ounces.
How much does she weigh? ______

Teacher's tips

Once you know 10% you can then calculate 5% by halving 10%, and 1% by dividing 10% by ten. Using this method you can break down any percentage into 10%, 5% and 1% chunks and calculate any answer!

Calculating percentages with a calculator

Practice

- Because a percentage can be written as a fraction or decimal, there are different ways of calculating percentages on a **calculator**.

As a fraction

Remember that a percentage can be written as a fraction 'out of 100' or 'divided by 100'.

To find **32% of £146** on a calculator, 32% can be keyed in as a **fraction**.

$\frac{32}{100} \times £146 = £46.72$ ← Key into the calculator 32 ÷ 100 and then × 146

Notice that the **multiplication key** is used in place of the word 'of'.

As a decimal

Another way is to write each percentage as a decimal. Remind yourself how on page 7.

To find **32% of £146** on a calculator, 32% can be keyed in as a **decimal**.

$0.32 \times £146 = £46.72$

Choose which way you like best and remember to use the multiplication key in place of the word 'of'.

- Always remember to check your answer, whichever way you do it.

32% of £146 = £46.72

<u>check</u>

32% is slightly less than one-third.

$\frac{1}{3}$ of £150 = £50

£46.72 is slightly less than **£50**.

So it is about right.

A different way of looking at it

There are different ways of solving percentage questions.

Here is another method.

Find 27% of 172.

First, find what **1%** of this number is.

172 divided by 100

Then multiply to find what **27%** is.

1.72 × 27

It does not matter which way this is done – the answer will be the same.

Check it

Check to get a rough idea of the size the answer should be. Always round the percentage and the number to make a rough calculation to see if the answer is about right.

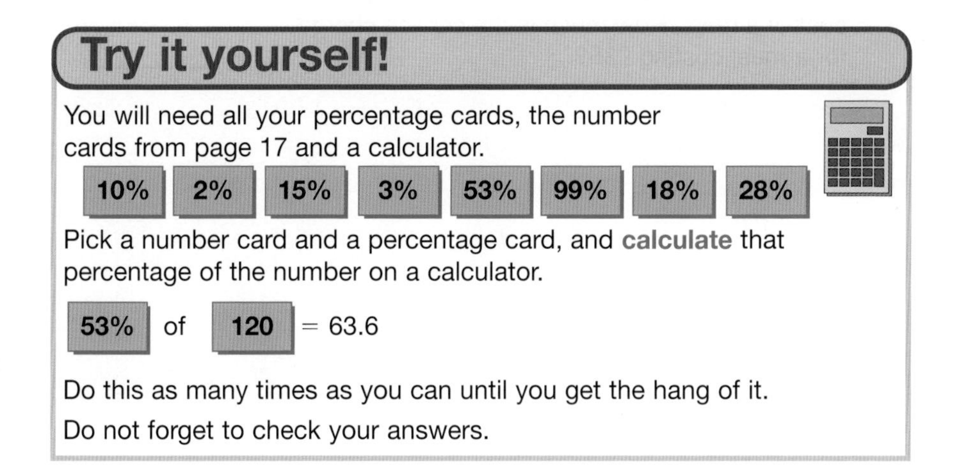

Try it yourself!

You will need all your percentage cards, the number cards from page 17 and a calculator.

10% **2%** **15%** **3%** **53%** **99%** **18%** **28%**

Pick a number card and a percentage card, and **calculate** that percentage of the number on a calculator.

53% of **120** = 63.6

Do this as many times as you can until you get the hang of it.

Do not forget to check your answers.

Clues and tips

Change the percentage to a decimal and then just multiply.

Decimal difficulties

Watch out for answers appearing on the calculator that do not make sense.

How much is £13.466839?

If you are talking about money, then round the answer to the nearest penny – £13.47.

What next?

Do you feel you understand the ideas in the book so far? Now is a good time to look back and go over the pages to check that you still understand.

For the next part of the book, you will need to be able to calculate percentages of any amounts with a calculator. If you need to, use your cards for more practice of this.

Try it yourself!

1. Calculate each of these percentages on a calculator.

32% of £60 ____	64% of £48 ____	88% of £97 ____
42% of 70 kg ____	18% of 112 kg ____	46% of 35 kg ____
17% of 87 ml ____	29% of 125 ml ____	82% of 305 ml ____
99% of 145 m ____	72% of 118 m ____	36% of 184 m ____

2. Solve these problems using a calculator.

In a sale you pay 84% of the ticket price.
The ticket price for a coat is £24.
How much is the sale price? ______

A man pays 28% of his earnings in tax.
He earns £15 000 in a year.
How much tax does he pay? ______

A baby girl weighs 86% of her expected weight.
If her expected weight was 130 ounces,
how much does she weigh? ______

A car is travelling at 54 mph. It slows down to travel at 67% of that speed.
How fast is the car travelling now? ______

I have £365 in my bank account.
I earn 3.5% interest on this money.
How much interest do I earn? ______

A restaurant adds a 12% service charge to the cost of a meal. How much is the service charge for a meal costing £35? ______

Teacher's tips

Press 'Clear' ('CE' on most calculators) before starting, and 'equals' (=) at the end, as some calculators keep a running total. Make a mental estimate and check the calculator's answer against this: always think whether the answer looks right.

Writing something as a percentage

Practice

- Up to now, almost every question in this book has had a percentage in it. Like these:

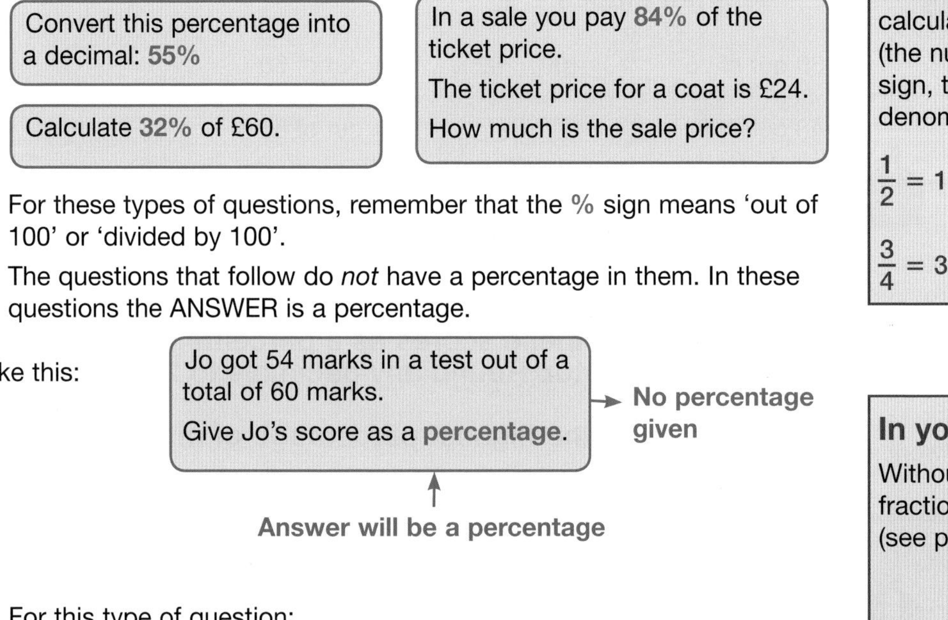

Convert this percentage into a decimal: **55%**

Calculate **32%** of £60.

In a sale you pay **84%** of the ticket price.
The ticket price for a coat is £24.
How much is the sale price?

For these types of questions, remember that the % sign means 'out of 100' or 'divided by 100'.

- The questions that follow do *not* have a percentage in them. In these questions the ANSWER is a percentage.

Like this:

Jo got 54 marks in a test out of a total of 60 marks.
Give Jo's score as a **percentage**.

No percentage given

Answer will be a percentage

- For this type of question:

a) write a number as a **fraction** of another
b) multiply by 100. **(Yes, it is that easy.)**

a) Jo got 54 out of 60. Write this as a **fraction**.
b) Then multiply by 100.

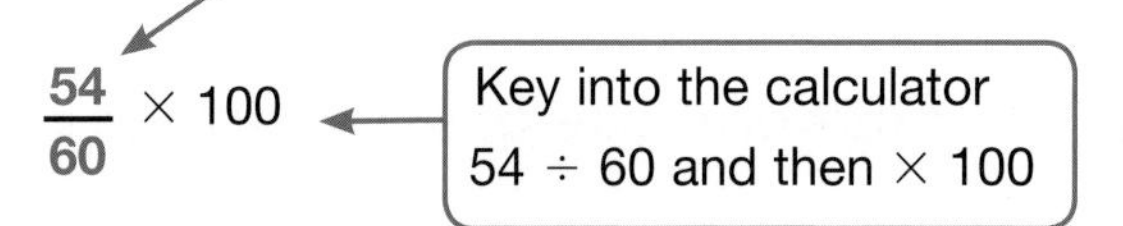

$\frac{54}{60} \times 100$

Key into the calculator
54 ÷ 60 and then × 100

Try this on a calculator. Do you get the answer 90%?
Notice that your ANSWER is a percentage.

Now try this one.

Rob got 34 marks in a test out of a total of 40 marks.
Give Rob's score as a percentage.

$\frac{34}{40} \times 100 = 85\%$

By changing both scores to percentages they can be compared to find out who scored the highest proportion of marks.

Fraction line

When looking at a fraction, think of the **line** separating the two numbers as a **division** sign.
When keying a fraction into a calculator, key in the top number (the numerator) and the divide sign, then the bottom number (the denominator). Like this:

$\frac{1}{2} = 1 \div 2$

$\frac{3}{4} = 3 \div 4$

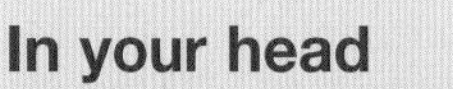

In your head

Without a calculator, change the fraction to its simplest form first (see page 5).

$\frac{54}{60} \xrightarrow{\div 6} \frac{9}{10}$

It is easier to multiply this by 100 in your head. Then, if possible, divide the denominator and 100 by the same number.

$\frac{9}{10} \times 100$ (10 ÷ 10, 100 ÷ 10)

$= 9 \times 10 = 90\%$

Clues and tips

When using a calculator, the answer might not be a whole number, e.g. 83.466839124.

Percentage answers should be rounded to one or two decimal places, e.g. 83.5% or 83.47%.

Without a calculator?

For question 3, remember to change each fraction to its simplest form first before multiplying by 100. If possible, divide the denominator and 100 by the same number, e.g. by 5, to make the numbers easier to work with.

What next?

If you are fine with this topic, go on to page 17.

If not, re-read the tips on page 5 about how to change a fraction to its simplest form.

Try it yourself!

**1. Give the first number as a percentage of the second number.
You can use a calculator. Round any decimals to 2 decimal places.**

60 out of 75	$\frac{60}{75} \times 100 = 80\%$	51 out of 60	______
48 out of 52	______	11 out of 55	______
58 out of 80	______	112 out of 120	______
45 out of 70	______	40 out of 65	______

**2. Give each of these scores as a percentage. You can use a calculator. Round any decimals to 2 decimal places.
Who scored the highest percentage of marks?**

Matt got 42 marks out of a total of 50 marks. ______

Richard got 64 marks out of a total of 70 marks. ______

Nicole got 73 marks out of a total of 80 marks. ______

Michelle got 33 marks out of a total of 40 marks. ______

Tom got 105 marks out of a total of 120 marks. ______

Jodie got 81 marks out of a total of 90 marks. ______

3. Answer these questions *without* using a calculator.

There were 150 people at a concert.
60 of the people were female.
What percentage were female? ______

There were 160 people at a funfair.
96 of the people were female.
What percentage were female? ______

Teacher's tips

Not using a calculator doesn't mean you have to do the calculation in your head! Some problems will be need to be written down. Whether you use a calculator or not, remember to use the % symbol for percentages.

Problems, problems

Practice

- Most people find percentages difficult because percentage problems and puzzles always look very different from each other.

12% of a 150 g chocolate bar is nuts. How many grams of nuts are there?

24 out of every 300 people in the country wear contact lenses. What is this as a percentage?

A bank paid Anna some interest on the £180 she had in the bank. It paid her £32. What is this as a percentage?

A pack of biscuits usually has 20 biscuits. In a new pack, 15% more biscuits are included. How many extra biscuits is that?

When you see a problem, do not panic!
Ask yourself these questions:

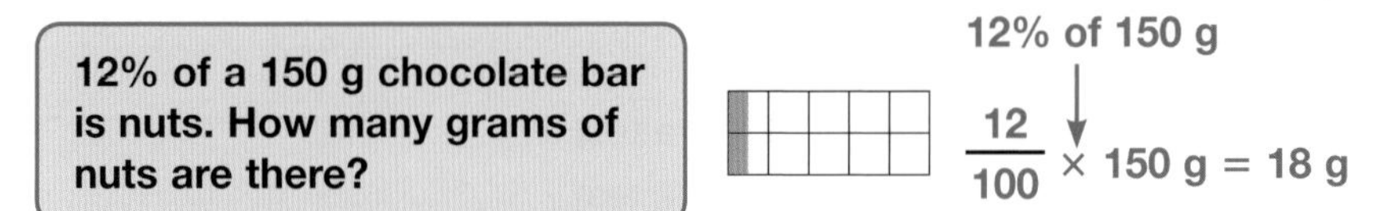

- If the question has a percentage in it, remember that the percentage sign means 'out of 100' or 'divided by 100'.

12% of a 150 g chocolate bar is nuts. How many grams of nuts are there?

12% of 150 g

$$\frac{12}{100} \times 150 \text{ g} = 18 \text{ g}$$

- If the ANSWER is to be a percentage, write the fraction and then multiply by 100.

24 out of every 300 people in the country wear contact lenses. What is this as a percentage?

$$\frac{24}{300} \times 100 = 8\%$$

Look carefully at every problem to work out which type it is. (Sometimes there might be an extra part to the question – these are looked at on the next few pages.)

Remember this

Do make sure that you read the question carefully to check you understand what it is asking for. Try to imagine the situation, drawing a small picture to help you, if you like.

Forgotten how?

If you have forgotten how to answer both types of questions, look at page 13 for the first type and page 15 for the second type.

Divide by 100 if the question contains a percentage.

Multiply by 100 to get a percentage ANSWER.

Clues and tips

Remember to write the unit or percentage sign in the answer.

Interest and VAT

Money that is kept in a bank or building society account, is usually given 'interest'. Interest is some extra money that is given, calculated as a percentage of the money that is in the account.

VAT stands for 'Value Added Tax'. Shops charge VAT on most items that they sell.

VAT is usually charged at a rate of 17.5%.

What next?

If you are happy with solving these types of problems, go on to page 19. From page 19 onwards you will find out about questions that involve percentage increases and decreases.

Try it yourself!

1. Solve these problems.

14% of a 250 g pot of yogurt is strawberries. How many grams of strawberries are there? $\frac{14}{100} \times 250\,g = 35\,g$

16 out of every 250 people in the country wear glasses. What is this as a percentage? ______

A bank paid Anna some interest on the £180 she had in the bank. It paid her £32.
What is this as a percentage? ______

A pack of biscuits usually has 20 biscuits. In a new pack, 15% more biscuits are included.
How many extra biscuits is that? ______

A drink is made with 18% of the total liquid being blackcurrant juice. If 350 ml of drink is made, how much is blackcurrant juice? ______

In a phone bill, 17.5% VAT is added to the cost of calls. If the total cost of calls is £58, how much is VAT? ______

2. Solve these problems, reading the question carefully.

45% of the 120 pupils in Class 1W are boys.
65% of the 80 pupils in Class 2G are boys.
Which class has more boys? ______

Megan scored 101 out of 130 in a test.
Rachel scored 188 out of 220 in a test.
Which girl had the higher percentage? ______

Teacher's tips

The most common mistake people make is misreading a question – always re-read to make sure you know what you're being asked to do! Work methodically, calculating the answer to each part in turn, comparing your answer to your mental estimate.

Percentage increases and decreases

Practice

- When something is made larger, it is **increased**.
  Things can be increased *by a percentage*. Look at these examples:

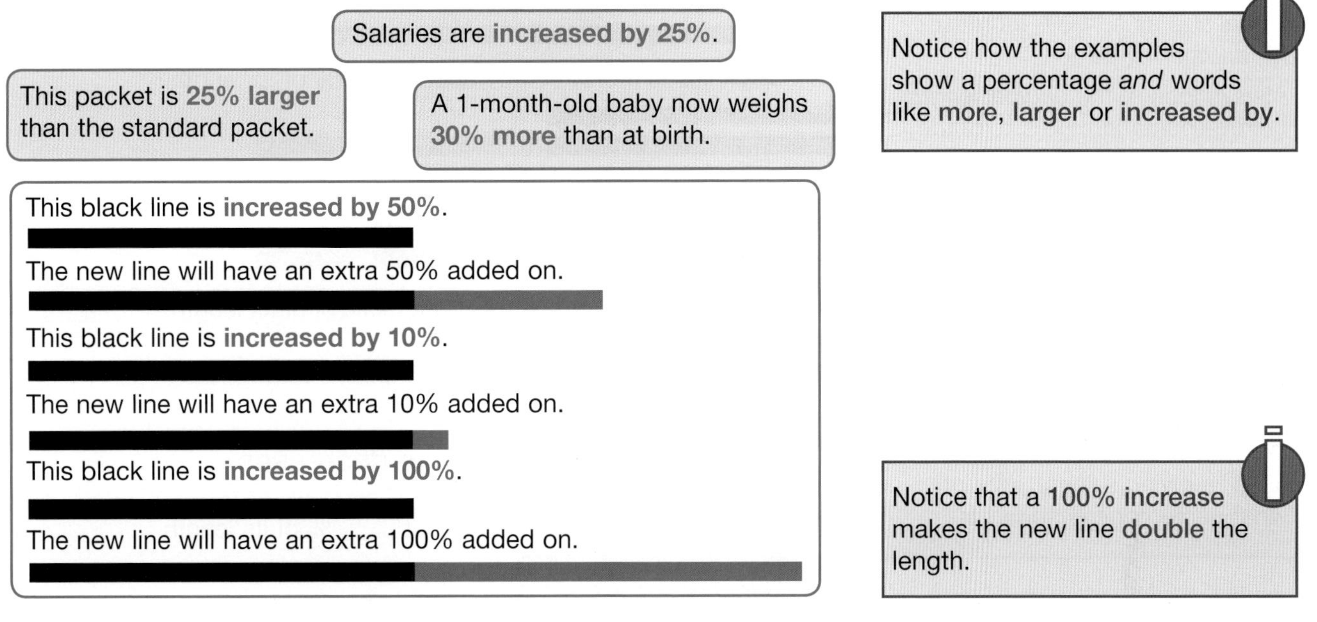

- When something is made smaller it is **decreased**.
  Things can be decreased *by a percentage*. Look at these examples:

Jim now weighs **40% less!**

All prices **reduced by 25%**.

A **12% decrease** in cases of measles last year.

Notice how these examples show a percentage *and* words like **less**, **reduced by** or **decreased by**.

This black line is **decreased by 50%**.

The new line will have 50% taken off.

This black line is **decreased by 10%**.

The new line will have 10% taken off.

This black line is **decreased by 100%**.

The new line will have 100% taken off.

Notice that a **100% decrease** leaves nothing.

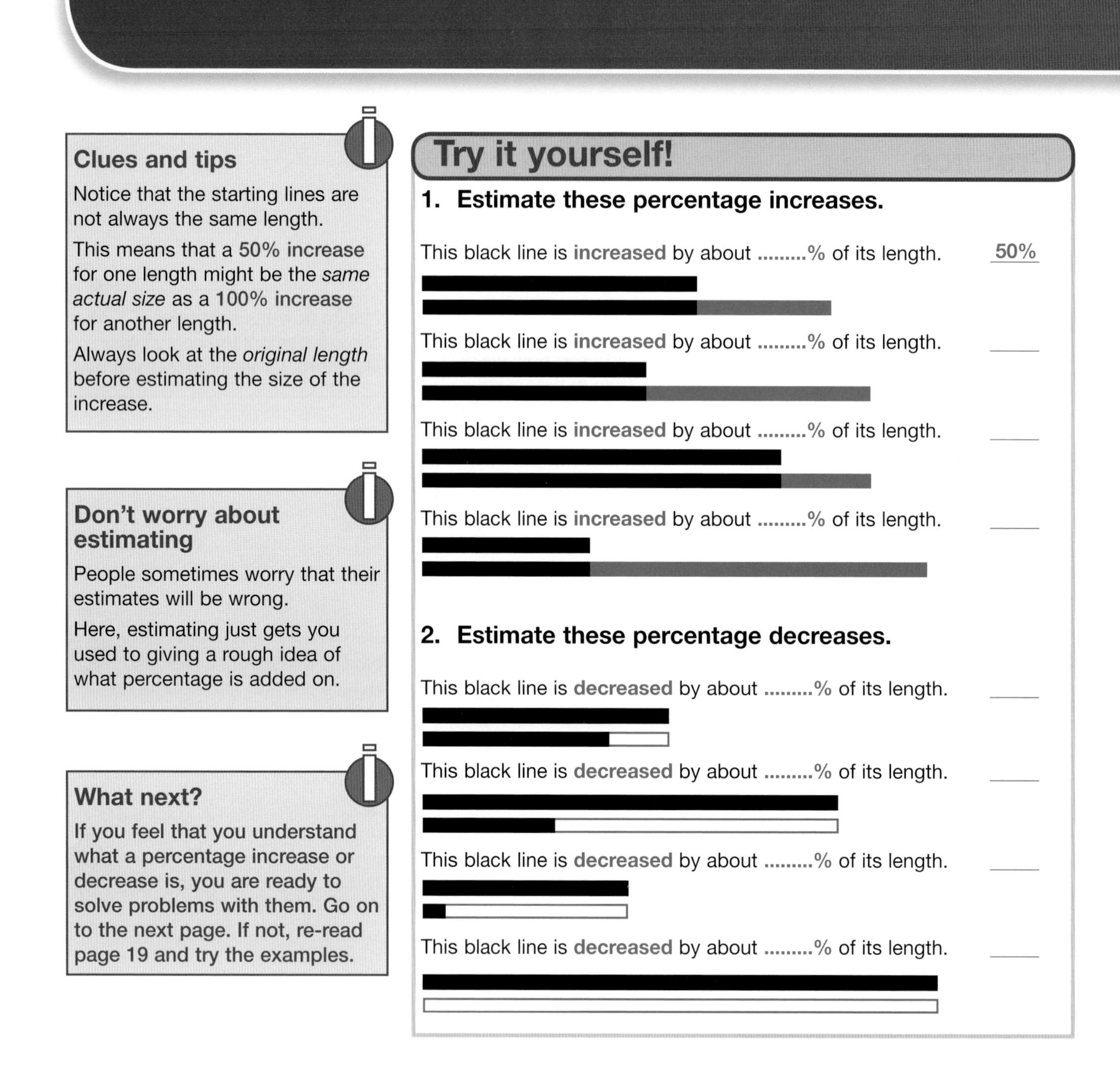

Clues and tips

Notice that the starting lines are not always the same length.

This means that a 50% increase for one length might be the *same actual size* as a 100% increase for another length.

Always look at the *original length* before estimating the size of the increase.

Don't worry about estimating

People sometimes worry that their estimates will be wrong.

Here, estimating just gets you used to giving a rough idea of what percentage is added on.

What next?

If you feel that you understand what a percentage increase or decrease is, you are ready to solve problems with them. Go on to the next page. If not, re-read page 19 and try the examples.

Try it yourself!

1. Estimate these percentage increases.

This black line is **increased** by about ....% of its length. 50%

This black line is **increased** by about ....% of its length. ______

This black line is **increased** by about ....% of its length. ______

This black line is **increased** by about ....% of its length. ______

2. Estimate these percentage decreases.

This black line is **decreased** by about ....% of its length. ______

This black line is **decreased** by about ....% of its length. ______

This black line is **decreased** by about ....% of its length. ______

This black line is **decreased** by about ....% of its length. ______

Teacher's tips

The increase or decrease percentage relates to the **original value** and not the answer. A £10 toy sold for £20 is a 100% increase; a £20 toy sold for £10 is a 50% decrease – even though both changed by £10.

Practice

- Now that you understand what a **percentage increase** is, you can solve percentage increase problems.
- This is all you have to do:

a) **calculate** the percentage of the amount given
b) **add** it on.

- Here is an example:

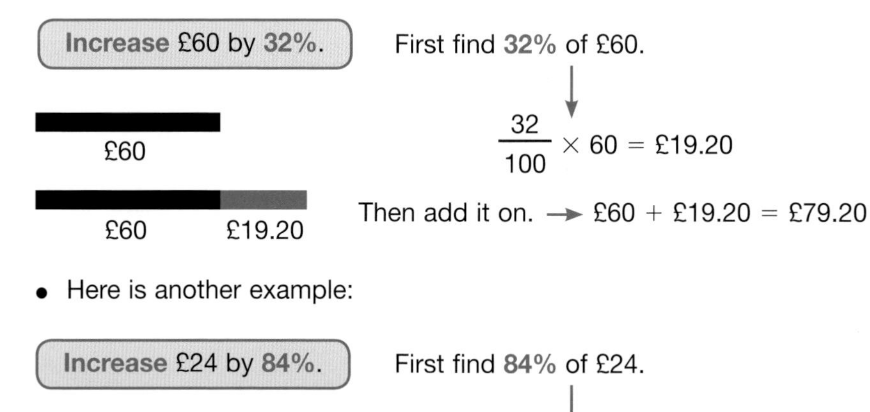

Increase £60 by **32%**.

First find **32%** of £60.

$$\frac{32}{100} \times 60 = £19.20$$

Then add it on. → £60 + £19.20 = £79.20

- Here is another example:

Increase £24 by **84%**.

First find **84%** of £24.

$$\frac{84}{100} \times 24 = £20.16$$

£24

£24 £20.16

Then add it on. → £24 + £20.16 = £44.16

- That is all there is to it, but sometimes the problems are worded in different ways. Try these.

The number of biscuits in a packet has been **increased by 15%**. There used to be **20** biscuits in a packet. How many are there now?

$$\frac{15}{100} \times 20 = 3$$

20 + 3 = 23

So now there are 23 biscuits altogether.

There were **4700** people living in a village last year. This year the population has **grown by 36%**. How many people live in the village now?

In a phone bill, VAT at **17.5% is added** to the cost of calls. The cost of calls is **£48**. How much will the bill be, including VAT?

You can do this already

The first step is easy – you can already do this. See page 13 to remind yourself how.

Use a calculator.

Remember that the percentage sign means 'out of 100' or 'divided by 100', so key in

32 ÷ 100

and then use the × key in place of the word 'of'.

Alternatively, you might prefer to key in the **decimal** 0.32 before multiplying by 60.

The answer will be the same whichever way you do it.

Watch out for words that show an increase, like 'grow', 'more', 'increases', 'added', 'extra', 'larger'.

Clues and tips

Look back at page 13 for a reminder on how to find a percentage of an amount.

Watch out

Be careful when it comes to adding on.

Make sure that you add the original amount and not the percentage.

Checking

Check to get a rough idea of the size that your answer should be. Always round the percentage and the number to make a rough calculation to see if your answer is about right.

What next?

Hopefully, you are finding it relatively easy to do. If you are, then you will find the percentage decrease questions on the next page just as easy. If you are still stuck, then you may need to practise finding percentages of amounts again. Follow the **Try it yourself!** activity on page 14 again.

Try it yourself!

1. Increase each price by the percentage shown.

Increase £80 by 24% ________ Increase £25 by 64% ________

Increase £48 by 82% ________ Increase £93 by 13% ________

Increase £134 by 47% ________ Increase £228 by 73% ________

Remember to check your answers by making a rough approximation.

2. Solve these percentage increase problems.

A car is travelling at a 58 mph. The driver increases the car's speed by 18%. What is the car's new speed? ________

Last year a man's mass was 58 kg. This year his mass has increased by 12%. What is the man's mass now? ________

The population of a village has grown by 35% from 1560 people ten years ago. What is the population of the village now? ________

In a phone bill, VAT at 17.5% is added to the total cost of calls. The total cost of calls is £68. How much will the bill be including VAT? ________

Remember to check your answers by making a rough approximation.

Teacher's tips

Remember the order to increase by a percentage: calculate what the percentage means as a value (how much money, weight, length, people etc), then add that value to the original amount.

Percentage decreases

Practice

- Now that you can solve **percentage increase** problems, you will find **percentage decrease** problems just as easy.
- This is all you have to do:

a) **calculate** the percentage of the amount given
b) **subtract** it.

- Here is an example:

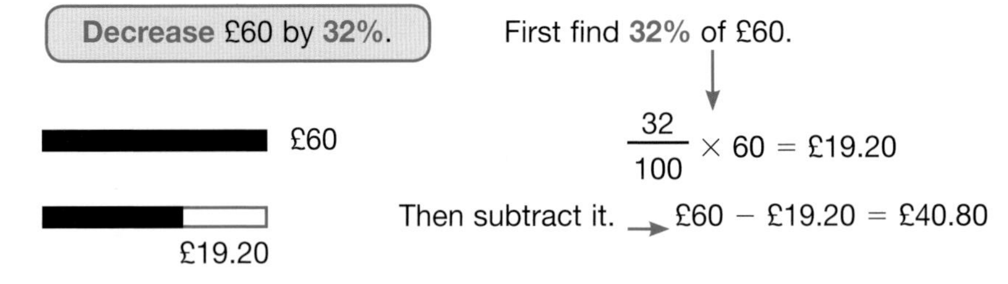

First find **32%** of £60.

$$\frac{32}{100} \times 60 = £19.20$$

Then subtract it. → £60 − £19.20 = £40.80

- Here is another example:

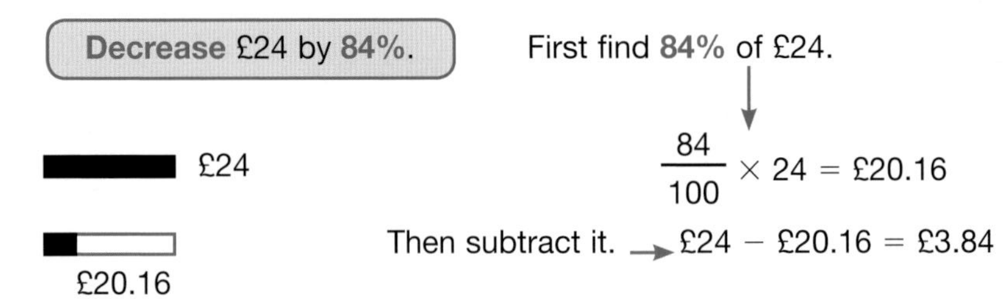

First find **84%** of £24.

$$\frac{84}{100} \times 24 = £20.16$$

Then subtract it. → £24 − £20.16 = £3.84

- That is all there is to it, but sometimes the problems are worded in different ways. Try these.

The number of biscuits in a packet has been **decreased by 15%**. There used to be **20** biscuits in a packet. How many are there now?

$$\frac{15}{100} \times 20 = 3$$

20 − 3 = 17

So now there are 17 biscuits altogether.

There were **4789** people living in a village last year. This year the population has **reduced by 36%**. How many people live in the village now?

A shop offers a **65% discount** on all ticket prices. A jacket's ticket price is **£28**. How much will the jacket cost in the sale?

You can do this already

The first step is easy – you can already do this. See page 13 to remind yourself how.

Use a calculator.

Remember that the percentage sign means 'out of 100' or 'divided by 100' so key in

32 ÷ 100

and then use the × key in place of the word 'of'.

Alternatively, you might prefer to key in the **decimal** 0.32 before multiplying by 60.

The answer will be the same whichever way you do it.

Watch out for words that show a decrease, like 'less', 'off', 'decreased by', 'reduced', 'left', 'discount'.

Clues and tips

Be careful when it comes to subtracting.

Make sure that you subtract from the original amount and not from the percentage.

Learn to look

When faced with a percentage problem, learn to look for words that indicate that it is a percentage decrease question, like 'decrease', 'discount', 'fallen', 'reduced'.

What next?

Hopefully, you are finding it relatively easy to do. If you are, then you will find the questions on the next page just as easy. If you are stuck, then you may need to practise finding percentages of amounts again. Follow the **Try it yourself!** activity on page 14 again.

Try it yourself!

1. Decrease each price by the percentage shown.

Decrease £80 by **24%** ________	**Decrease** £25 by **64%** ________
Decrease £48 by **82%** ________	**Decrease** £93 by **13%** ________
Decrease £134 by **47%** ________	**Decrease** £228 by **73%** ________

Remember to check your answers by making a rough approximation.

2. Solve these percentage decrease problems.

A car is travelling at a **58 mph**. The driver **decreases** the car's speed by **18%**. What is the car's new speed? ________

Last year a man's mass was **58 kg**. This year his mass has **fallen** by **12%**. What is the man's mass now? ________

The population of a village has **dropped** by **35%** from **1560** people ten years ago. What is the population of the village now? ________

A person pays **22%** of his earnings in tax. He earns **£28 000** each year. How much money will he have **left** after he has paid tax? ________

Remember to check your answers by making a rough approximation.

Teacher's tips

To decrease by a percentage is the same but subtracting the amount: calculate what the percentage means as a value (how much money, weight, length, people etc), then subtract that value to the original amount.

Increasing and decreasing more than once

Practice

- **Percentage increases** and **decreases** occur in many situations in **real life**. Look at these examples:

When a person puts money into a savings account, they receive an extra percentage of that money called **interest**.

In January, a shop reduces its prices for the sale. Those items not sold by February are reduced by a further percentage.

- In both examples, a percentage increase or decrease occurs *more than once*.

Emily has £3000 in a bank. She receives 5% interest each year.
After Year 1:
she receives **5%** of **£3000** (= £150), which is added to her money.
After Year 2:
she receives **5%** of **£3150** (= £157.50), which is then added.

Notice that the first increase of 5% (£150) is *not the same amount* as the second increase of 5% (£157.50).

A dress cost £200 in December. In January it is reduced by 15%. In February it is reduced by a further 15%.
January:
The cost is reduced from **£200** by **15%** (£30 reduction).
February:
The cost is reduced from **£170** by **15%** (£25.50 reduction).

Notice that the first decrease of 15% (£30) is *not the same amount* as the second decrease of 15% (£25.50).

- People often make the mistake of thinking that a percentage increase or decrease will be the same as the one that follows it.
- Is an increase of 10% followed by a further increase of 10% *the same* as an increase of 20%? Look at this example:

Increase **£300** by **10%** — **10%** of **£300** = £30, £300 + £30 = **£330**

then

Increase **£330** by **10%** — **10%** of **£330** is £33, £330 + £33 = **£363**

Is this the same as ... ?

Increase **£300** by **20%** — **20%** of **£330** is £60, £330 + £60 = **£360**

The answer is **NO**. They are *not* the same.

Interest

Money kept in a bank or building society account, is usually given **interest**.

Interest is some extra money that is given, calculated as a percentage of the money that is in the account.

Don't be fooled

Imagine that there was a choice between two bank accounts.

One paid **8%** interest **each year** for **2 years**, and another paid out **16%** interest **after 2 years**. Would both accounts give the same amount of interest after 2 years?

The difference between the two amounts on the left is £3.

More confident with percentages now?

Tick the following topics you feel confident with:

Part 1

- Estimating percentages (pages 3–4) ☐
- Writing percentages as fractions out of 100 and in their simplest form (pages 5–6) ☐
- Writing percentages as fractions and decimals (pages 7–8) ☐
- Calculating percentages in your head (pages 9–12) ☐
- Calculating percentages with a calculator (pages 13–14) ☐

Part 2

- Writing one number as a percentage of another (pages 15–16) ☐
- Solving percentage problems (pages 17–18) ☐
- Estimating percentage increases and decreases (pages 19–20) ☐
- Calculating percentage increases and decreases (pages 21–24) ☐
- Increasing and decreasing more than once (pages 25–26) ☐

Read through any pages again to make sure that you understand.

Why not look at other books in this series to help you with areas you still might be unsure about?

Try it yourself!

1. Which is more and by how much?

£2000 increased by 15%, followed by a further increase of 15%	OR	£2000 increased by 30%?

15% of £2000 = £300
15% of £2300 = £345
Now worth £2645 ← More by £45

30% of £2000 = £600
Now worth £2600

£5000 increased by 35%, followed by a further increase of 35%	OR	£5000 increased by 70%?

£4000 decreased by 30%, followed by a further decrease of 30%	OR	£4000 decreased by 60%?

£9000 decreased by 15%, followed by a further decrease of 15%	OR	£9000 decreased by 30%?

Teacher's tips

When more than once percentage change happens the second change applies to the result of the first change, **not** the original value. There are no short cuts – you must work out each answer in turn!

Solving simple equations

Practice

This section is going to look at **equations**.

- An equation always has an equals sign. What is on one side of the equals sign is worth the same as what is on the other side.

  Like:

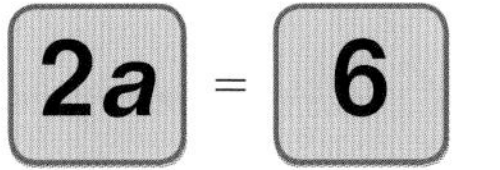

or

$2a$ is worth the same as 6 $2y + 3$ is worth the same as $4y - 1$

- If only one letter is used in an equation, it is possible to **solve the equation**.

  Solving the equation means finding out what number the letter stands for. It is like cracking a code.

- Look at each of the following equations. Imagine that a number is hidden underneath each letter. What number would this be to make each number sentence correct?

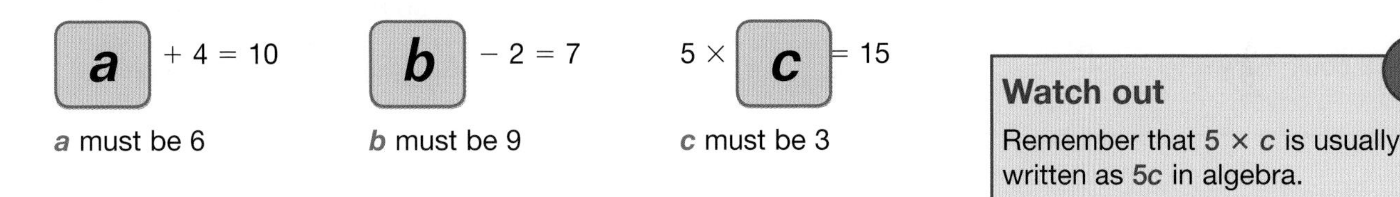

a must be 6 b must be 9 c must be 3

This is called solving the equation.

- Use the cut-out cards to make each of these equations. Solve each of them.

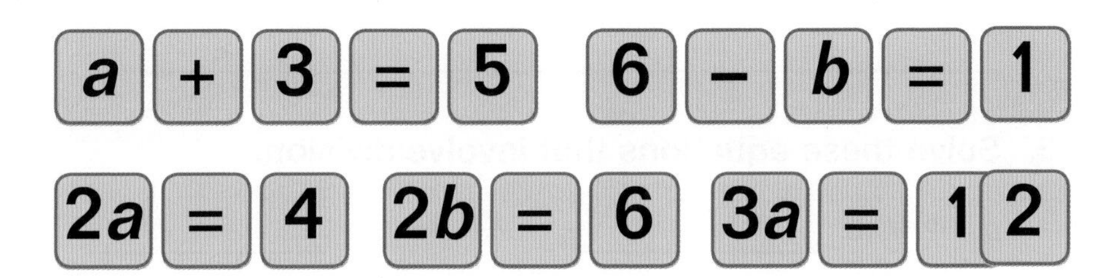

- Check your solutions by **substituting** the number for the letter on one side to see if it equals what is on the other side.
- Remember this:

  solving the equation – finding out what number a letter stands for in an equation

Puzzles

Being able to solve equations can help us with all kinds of problems and puzzles.

Look at this puzzle:

I think of a number and add 5 to it. The answer is 14. What is my number?

Let us call the number n (or any other letter we choose).

This puzzle can be written as $n + 5 = 14$

It can help us to see that $n = 9$

Watch out

Remember that $5 \times c$ is usually written as $5c$ in algebra.

Crack the code

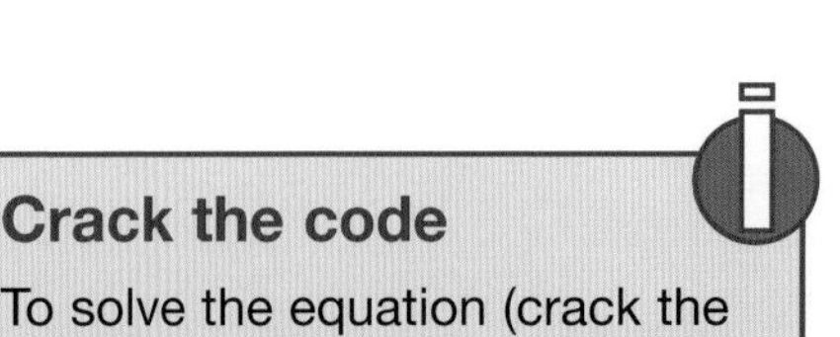

To solve the equation (crack the code), imagine what number must be hidden beneath each letter to make the number sentence true.

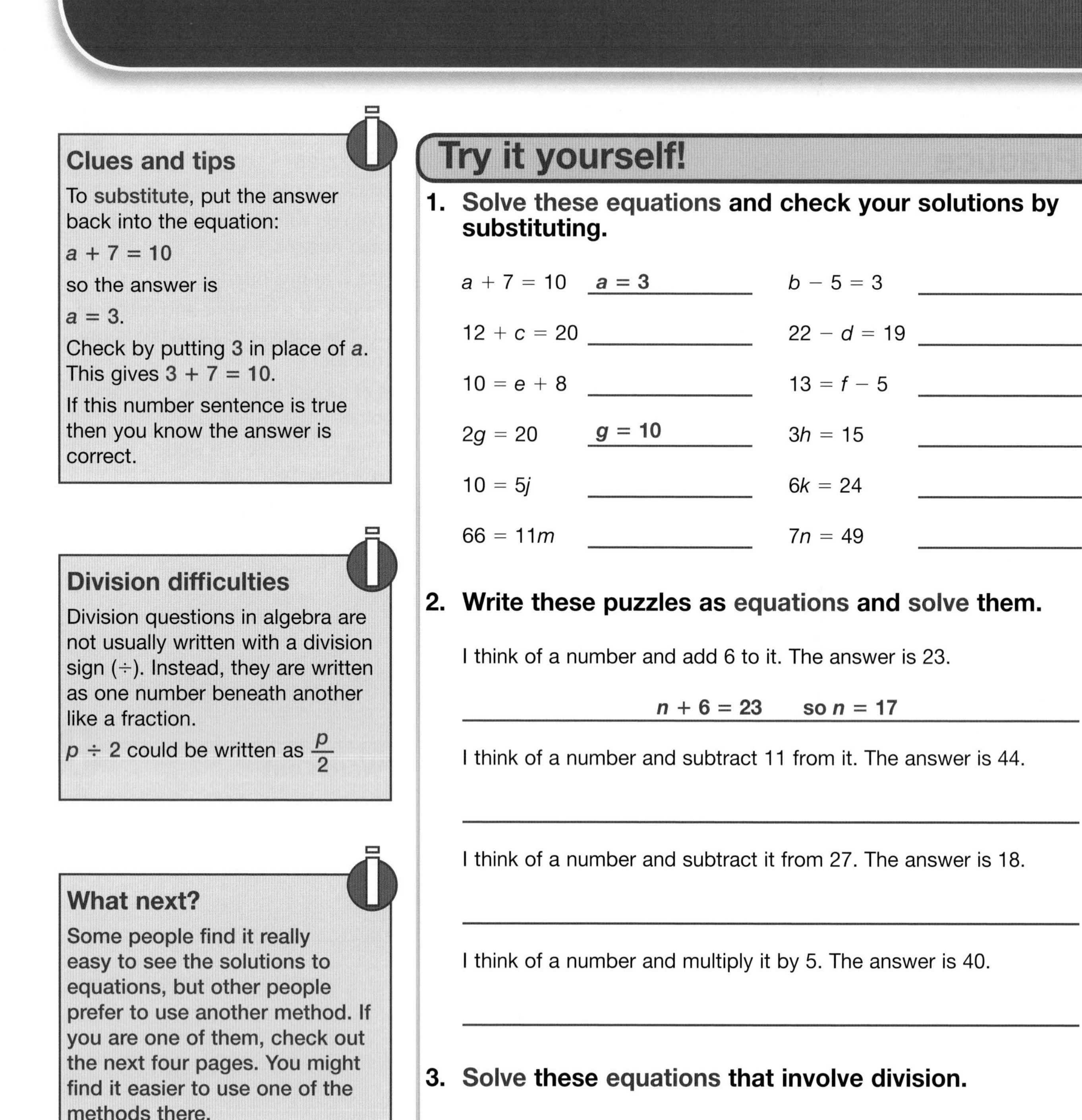

Clues and tips

To substitute, put the answer back into the equation:

$a + 7 = 10$

so the answer is

$a = 3$.

Check by putting 3 in place of a. This gives $3 + 7 = 10$.

If this number sentence is true then you know the answer is correct.

Division difficulties

Division questions in algebra are not usually written with a division sign (÷). Instead, they are written as one number beneath another like a fraction.

$p \div 2$ could be written as $\frac{p}{2}$

What next?

Some people find it really easy to see the solutions to equations, but other people prefer to use another method. If you are one of them, check out the next four pages. You might find it easier to use one of the methods there.

Try it yourself!

1. Solve these equations and check your solutions by substituting.

$a + 7 = 10$	**$a = 3$**	$b - 5 = 3$	______
$12 + c = 20$	______	$22 - d = 19$	______
$10 = e + 8$	______	$13 = f - 5$	______
$2g = 20$	**$g = 10$**	$3h = 15$	______
$10 = 5j$	______	$6k = 24$	______
$66 = 11m$	______	$7n = 49$	______

2. Write these puzzles as equations and solve them.

I think of a number and add 6 to it. The answer is 23.

$n + 6 = 23$ so $n = 17$

I think of a number and subtract 11 from it. The answer is 44.

______

I think of a number and subtract it from 27. The answer is 18.

______

I think of a number and multiply it by 5. The answer is 40.

______

3. Solve these equations that involve division.

$p \div 2 = 10$	______	$q \div 4 = 5$	______
$27 \div r = 3$	______	$45 \div s = 9$	______
$t \div 4 = 10$	______	$u \div 6 = 8$	______

Teacher's tips

Some people are distracted by the letter choice – don't be. The letter isn't important, and any can be used. Think of the letter as a code for a hidden number.

Solving equations by balancing

Practice

- Sometimes it is not easy to spot the solution to an **equation**.
- There are two different ways of solving these. This page looks at a method of **solving equations** using ideas of **balancing**.

  Both sides of an equation are worth the same – they balance.

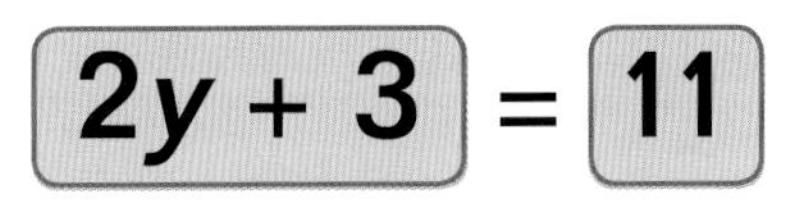

$2y + 3 = 11$

$2y + 3$ is worth the same as 11
$2y + 3$ and 11 balance

Remember this

Remember that when adding and subtracting parts of an expression, you can only add or subtract a **number** from a **number** or a **letter** from the same **letter**.

Like this …

$2a + 5 - 2$
$= 2a + 3$
$4b - 8 + 8$

THE RULES

- Whatever is done to one side of an equation, must be done to the other so that both sides still balance.
- You can add, subtract, multiply or divide one side of an equation – but you must do the same to the other side, too.
- Aim to get the **letter** on its own **on one side** and the numbers on the other side.
- To get rid of something from one side, do the opposite. If it is an **add** then **subtract**, if it is a **times** then **divide** and vice versa.

Watch out

Here, because numbers are being added and subtracted, the letters do not change.

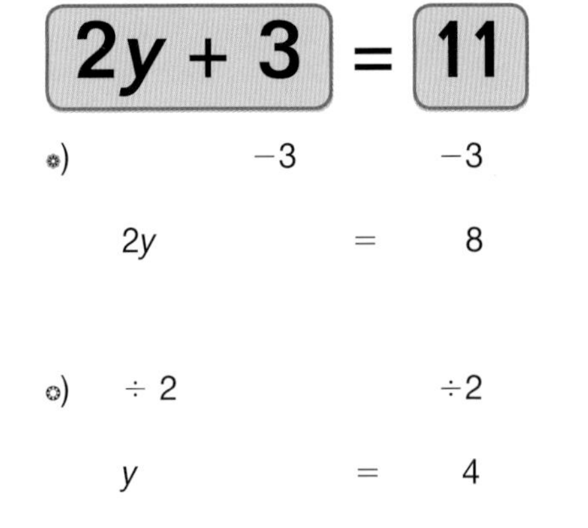

$2y + 3 = 11$

a) -3 -3

$2y = 8$

a) Get rid of the **+3** on the left. (Do the opposite by subtracting 3 and do the same to both sides.)

b) $\div 2$ $\div 2$

$y = 4$

b) Get rid of the **× 2** on the left. (Do the opposite by dividing by 2, and do the same to both sides.)

Watch out

$2y$ is the same as $y \times 2$, so to get just y we **divide** both sides by **2**.

- This has **solved the equation**. The solution is $y = 4$.
- Check the **solution** by **substituting** the number for the letter on one side to see if it equals what is on the other side.

$2y + 3 = 11$

$y = 4$ so $2 \times 4 + 3$ should equal 11.
$8 + 3$ *does* equal 11, so the solution $y = 4$ is correct.

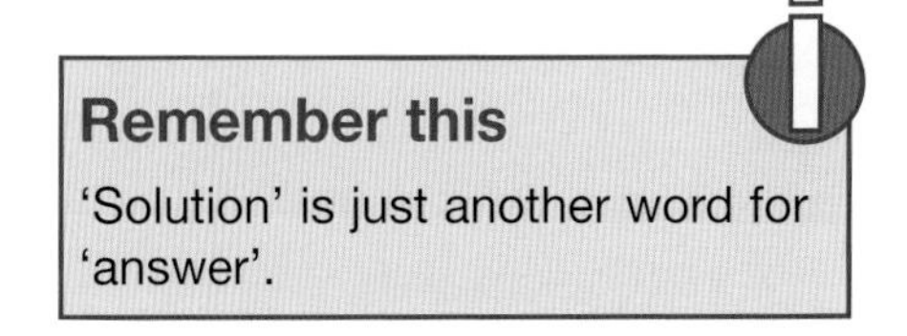

Remember this

'Solution' is just another word for 'answer'.

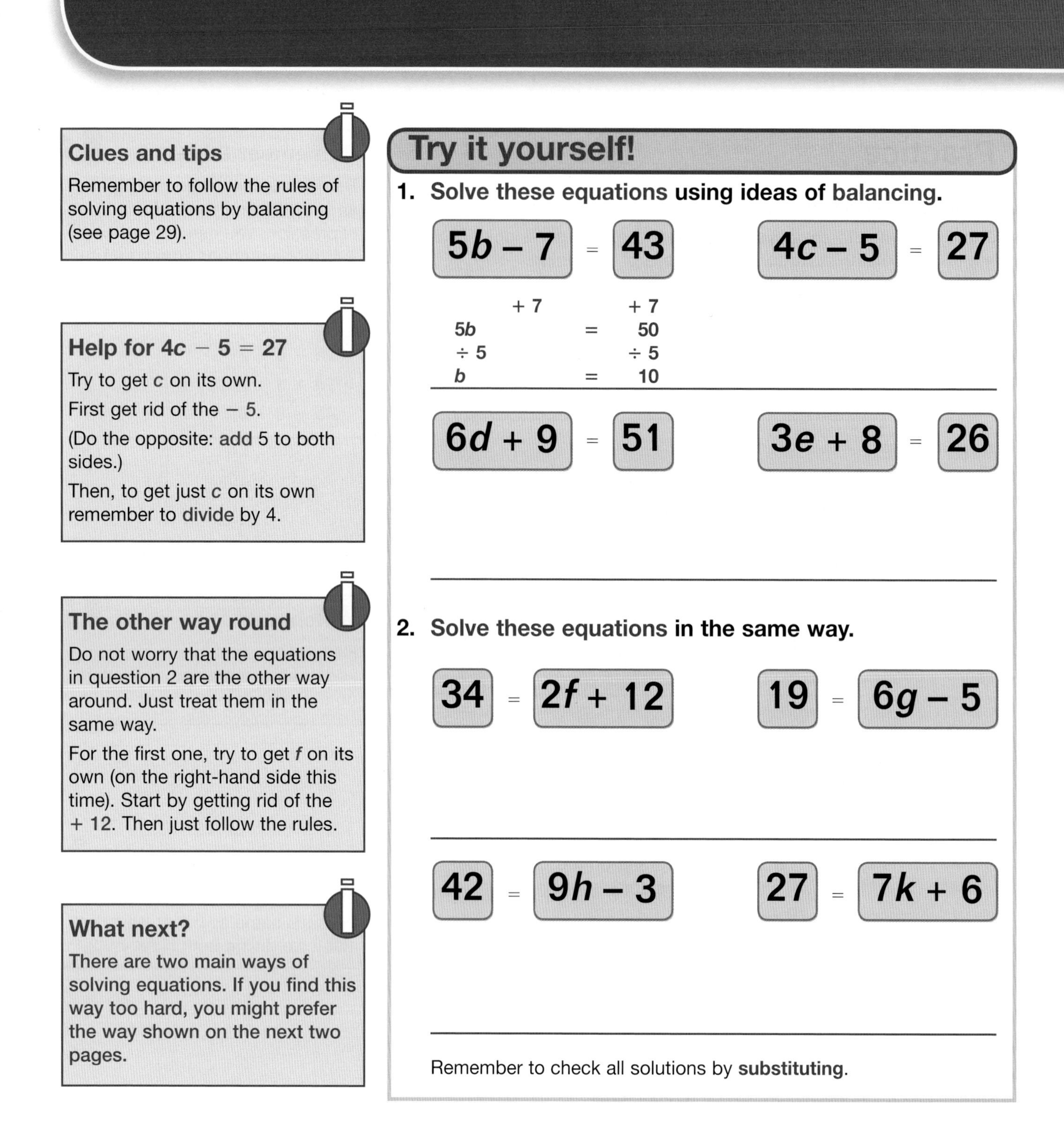

Clues and tips

Remember to follow the rules of solving equations by balancing (see page 29).

Help for $4c - 5 = 27$

Try to get c on its own.

First get rid of the $- 5$.

(Do the opposite: add 5 to both sides.)

Then, to get just c on its own remember to divide by 4.

The other way round

Do not worry that the equations in question 2 are the other way around. Just treat them in the same way.

For the first one, try to get f on its own (on the right-hand side this time). Start by getting rid of the $+ 12$. Then just follow the rules.

What next?

There are two main ways of solving equations. If you find this way too hard, you might prefer the way shown on the next two pages.

Try it yourself!

1. Solve these equations using ideas of balancing.

$5b - 7 = 43$

$+ 7$		$+ 7$
$5b$	$=$	50
$\div 5$		$\div 5$
b	$=$	10

$4c - 5 = 27$

$6d + 9 = 51$

$3e + 8 = 26$

2. Solve these equations in the same way.

$34 = 2f + 12$

$19 = 6g - 5$

$42 = 9h - 3$

$27 = 7k + 6$

Remember to check all solutions by **substituting**.

Teacher's tips

Remember '=' means 'is the same as'. Always keep both sides of an equation 'the same as' the other, by doing the same to both sides. If you don't the two sides won't equal, and the equation is wrong.

Solving equations using inverses

Practice

- Some people prefer this way to **solve equations**.
- To use this method needs an understanding of **inverses**.
  Every operation has an inverse (or opposite).

The inverse of addition is subtraction	$+$	$-$
The inverse of subtraction is addition	$-$	$+$
The inverse of multiplication is division	$\times$	$\div$
The inverse of division is multiplication	$\div$	$\times$

- The idea of this method is to work backwards, using inverses. Think of this equation as a trail of instructions, *starting with the letter*.

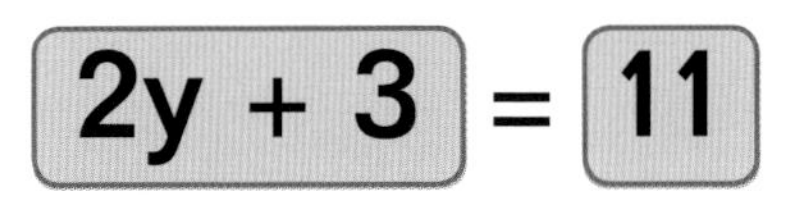

Start with y → multiply it by 2 → then add 3 → to get to 11

Now write this backwards, starting at 11.

to get to y ← divide by 2 ← subtract 3 ← Start with 11

Notice that the inverse has been used for each operation and that the order is reversed.

These new instructions could be written as …

$$(11 - 3) \div 2 = y$$

… and then find y.

$(11 - 3) \div 2 = y$

$8 \div 2 = y$

$4 = y$ so y must equal 4.

- This has **solved the equation**. The solution is $y = 4$.
- As always, check the solution by **substituting** the number for the letter on one side to see if it equals what is on the other side.

$y = 4$ so $2 \times 4 + 3$ should equal 11.
$8 + 3$ *does* equal 11, so the solution $y = 4$ is correct.

BODMAS

Have you ever heard of the word BODMAS?

This is a way of helping you remember the order in which calculations are carried out.

Brackets	(Do anything in brackets first)
Other	(Do other things, including squaring or finding the square root)
Divide Multiply	(Then divide or multiply numbers)
Add Subtract	(Finally add or subtract numbers)

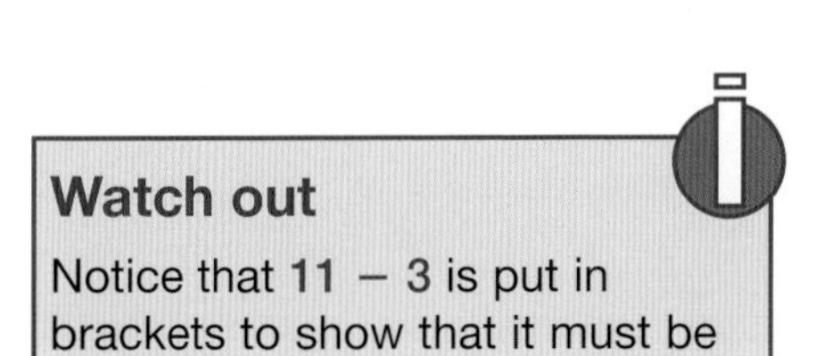

Watch out

Notice that $11 - 3$ is put in brackets to show that it must be worked out first.

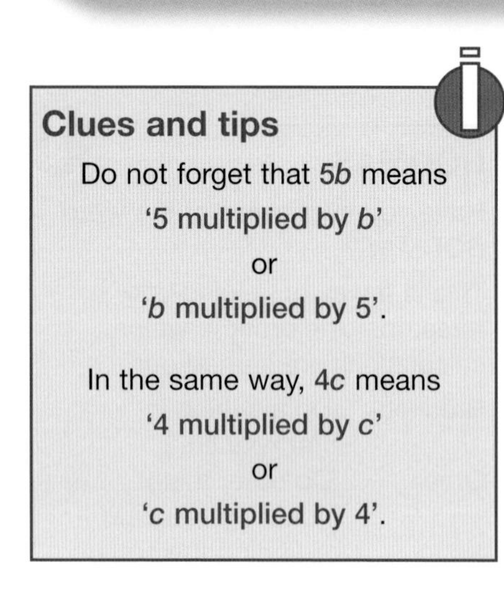

Clues and tips

Do not forget that $5b$ means '5 multiplied by b' or 'b multiplied by 5'.

In the same way, $4c$ means '4 multiplied by c' or 'c multiplied by 4'.

Always check the solution by substituting

There should be no need to look at the answers in the back. You should know whether the solution is right or wrong. See page 31 for a reminder of how to check.

What next?

Look back over the last four pages. Do you prefer the balancing method or the inverse method? It does not matter which method you use as long as you can get to the right answer every time.

Try it yourself!

1. Solve these equations using inverses.

Start with b →	multiply by 5 →	subtract 7 →	to get to 43
to get to b ←	divide by 5 ←	add 7 ←	Start with 43

$(43 + 7) \div 5 = b$

$50 \div 5 = b$

$\underline{10 = b}$ or $\underline{b = 10}$

Start with c →

$6d + 9 = 51$

2. Solve these equations. Do your working out *on paper*.

$5e + 8 = 33$	$36 = 3f + 12$	$30 = 8g - 10$
$32 = 7h - 3$	$31 = 2j + 13$	$38 = 5k - 17$
$24 = 5m - 6$	$65 = 7n + 16$	$57 = 8p - 7$

Remember to check all solutions by **substituting.**

Teacher's tips

Sometimes you may see the letter swapping sides of the equation during the calculation. You may choose to do this, or keep it on the same side – it doesn't matter as long as you keep the equation equal.

Solving more complex equations

Practice

- Some equations are harder as they may include **brackets**.
- If an equation has brackets, it is usually easier to **expand** them first and then **solve** the equation as before.

- Once the equation is without brackets, solve it using **balancing** or **inverses** – whichever you prefer.

- Sometimes, when solving equations, the solution might be a **decimal** rather than a whole number. Look at the method you prefer. Notice how below, 42 is divided by 4.
A calculator could be used to find the solution.

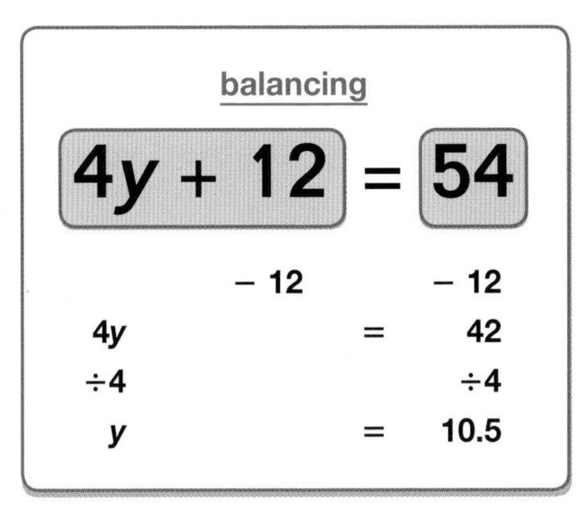

- As always, check the solution by **substituting** the number for the letter on one side to see if it equals what is on the other side.

$4y + 12 = 54$

$y = 10.5$ so $4 \times 10.5 + 12$ should equal 54.
$42 + 12$ *does* equal 54, so $y = 10.5$ is correct.

inverses

Start with y → multiply by 4 → add 12 → to get to 54
to get to y ← divide by 4 ← subtract 12 ← Start with 54

$(54 - 12) \div 4 = y$
$42 \div 4 = y$
so $y = 10.5$

Solving equations with brackets

It *is* possible to solve equations *without* **expanding the brackets.**
Your teacher might have taught this method. It does not matter which method is used as long as the correct answer is reached each time.

Decimal difficulties

Use a calculator to divide the numbers. If the decimal has many digits after the decimal point, like 4.5725163485, then just round it to 2 **decimal places** (so that the answer has 2 digits after the decimal point).

Clues and tips

When expanding brackets, it helps to draw arrows as a reminder to multiply the part outside by *every part* inside.

In question 2, round the answer if it is a decimal with lots of digits after the decimal point, e.g. 3.583625167 can be written as 3.58.

What next?

Hopefully, you are getting much better at solving equations. If you want more practice at solving equations with decimal solutions, you can make up your own. Just write down an expression and put it equal to any number you choose. Then try to solve it. To check whether you are right, use substitution.

Try it yourself!

1. Expand the brackets of these equations first.

Then **solve** each equation, using either the **balancing** or the **inverses** method. Do your working out *on paper*.

$5(a + 2) = 30$ $\quad 3(b + 4) = 15$ $\quad 2(c - 5) = 6$

$\mathbf{5a + 10 = 30}$

$a =$ ______

$4(h - 3) = 28$ $\quad 9(j + 1) = 36$ $\quad 2(3k - 5) = 32$

$5(2m - 6) = 30$ $\quad 32 = 2(5n + 6)$ $\quad 15 = 3(4p - 7)$

Remember to check all solutions by **substituting**.

2. Solve these equations using whichever method you choose.

These equations have **decimal** solutions.

Do your working out *on paper*. Use a calculator.

$4e + 8 = 18$ $\quad 10 = 12f + 1$ $\quad 2 = 5g - 4$

$2(h - 3) = 7$ $\quad 4(j + 8) = 58$ $\quad 5(2k - 1) = 38$

$3m - 6 = 41$ $\quad 7(n + 4) = 53$ $\quad 6(3p - 7) = 55$

Remember to check all solutions by **substituting**.

Teacher's tips

Use BODMAS – always do anything in brackets first. Remember whatever value or action is outside the bracket applies to each number/letter inside. Don't get caught out expanding 4(a + 3) to 4a +3, this is wrong! (It's 4a +12).

Letters on both sides of an equation

Practice

- Some equations have a letter on both sides, like this:

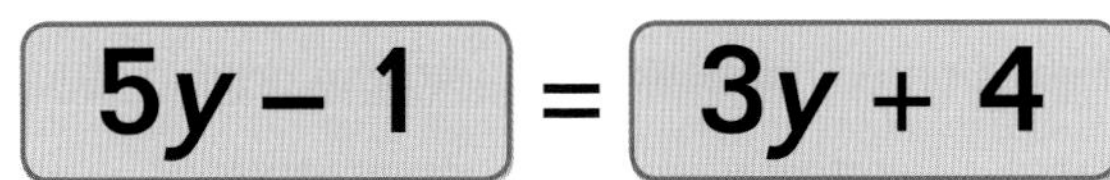

To **solve equations** like these, use **balancing** to get the letters all on one side first.

- So, with our example, to get all the y's on one side of the equation (it does not matter which side) *add or subtract the same number of y's from both sides*.

$$5y - 1 = 3y + 4$$

To get rid of **3y** from the right, **subtract 3y** from both sides.

$$\begin{array}{lcl} 5y - 1 & = & 3y + 4 \\ -3y & & -3y \\ 2y - 1 & = & 4 \end{array}$$

- This is a new equation with the letter y on one side only. This new **equivalent** equation can be solved in the same way as before, using either the **balancing** or **inverses** method.

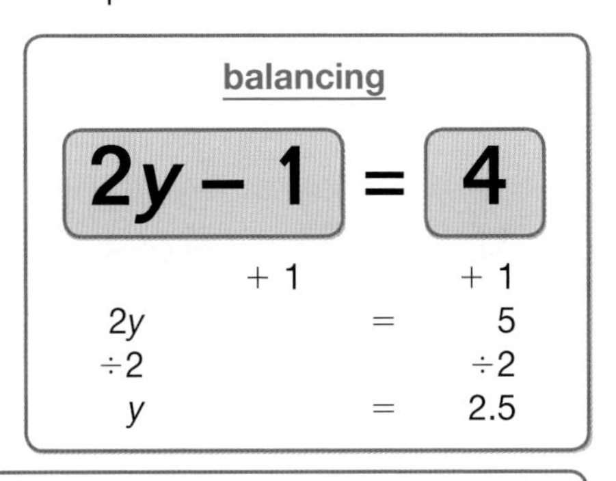

inverses

$$2y - 1 = 4$$

Start with y → multiply by 2 → subtract 1 → to get to 4

to get to y ← divide by 2 ← add 1 ← Start with 4

$(4 + 1) \div 2 = y$

$5 \div 2 = y$

so $y = 2.5$

- As always, check the solution by **substituting** the number for the letter on one side to see if it equals what is on the other side.

$$5y - 1 = 3y + 4$$

$y = 2.5$

$5 \times$ **2.5** $- 1$ should equal $3 \times$ **2.5** $+ 4$

$12.5 - 1 = 11.5 \qquad 7.5 + 4 = 11.5$

They are both equal, so $y = 2.5$ is correct.

Clues and tips

Remind yourself about the **balancing** methods by looking again at pages 29 and 30. Make sure you read THE RULES.

Remember this

Remember that when adding and subtracting parts of an expression only add or subtract a **number** from a **number** or a **letter** from the same **letter**. Like this:

$5a - 5 + 2a$

$= 7a - 5$

$4b + 8 - 4b = 8$

Watch out

The new equation is **equivalent** to (worth the same as) the original one, so it will have the same solution (and it is much easier to solve).

Remember this

Notice that the solution is substituted into the *original* equation.

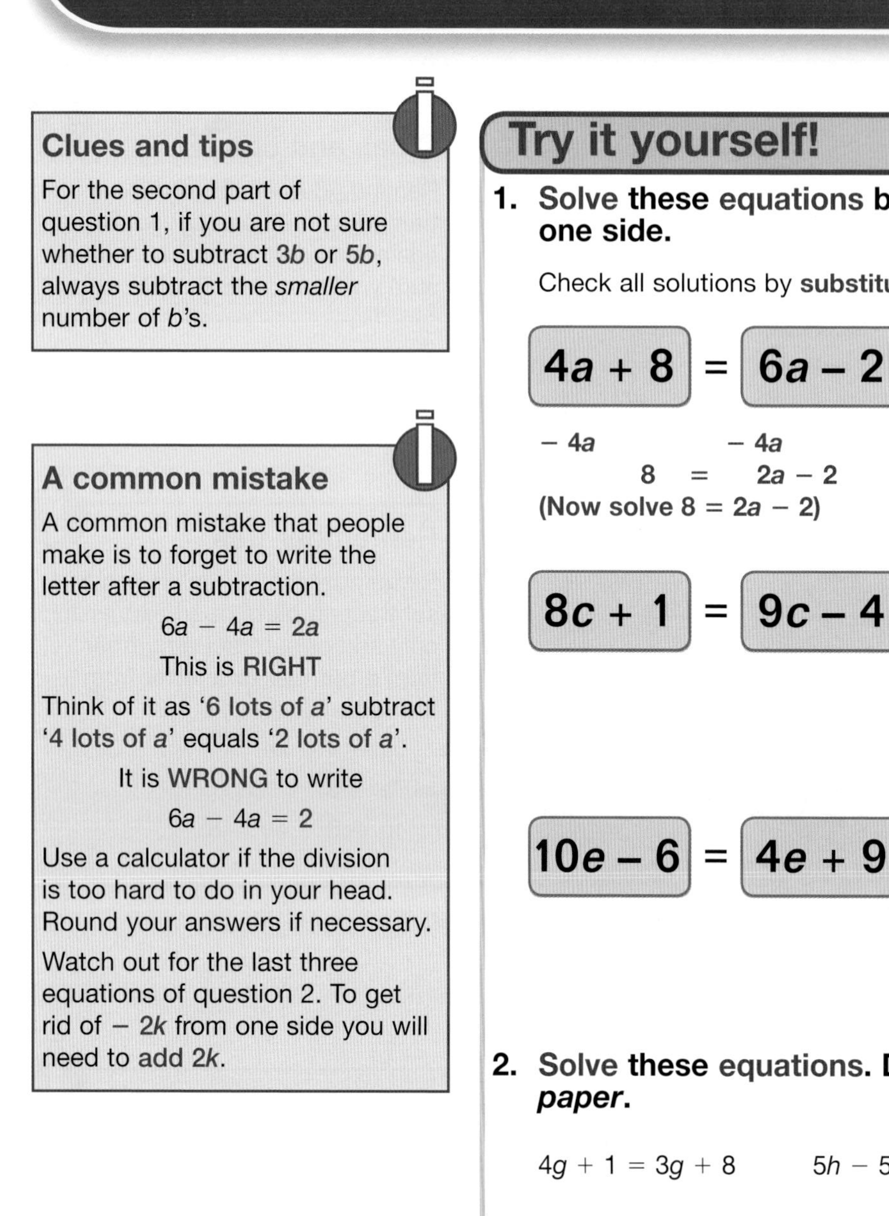

Clues and tips

For the second part of question 1, if you are not sure whether to subtract $3b$ or $5b$, always subtract the *smaller* number of b's.

A common mistake

A common mistake that people make is to forget to write the letter after a subtraction.

$6a - 4a = 2a$

This is RIGHT

Think of it as '6 lots of a' subtract '4 lots of a' equals '2 lots of a'.

It is WRONG to write

$6a - 4a = 2$

Use a calculator if the division is too hard to do in your head. Round your answers if necessary.

Watch out for the last three equations of question 2. To get rid of $-2k$ from one side you will need to add $2k$.

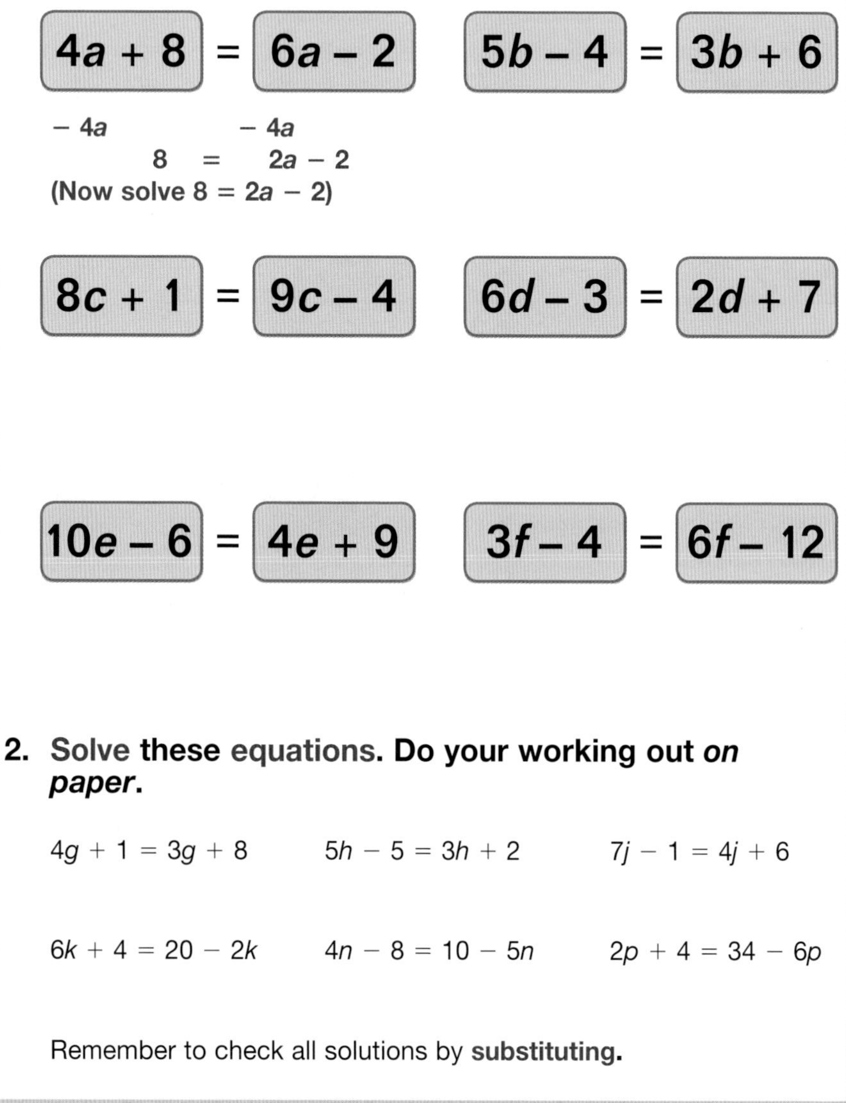

Try it yourself!

1. Solve these equations by first getting the letters on one side.

Check all solutions by **substituting** into the original equation.

$4a + 8 = 6a - 2$ $\qquad$ $5b - 4 = 3b + 6$

$-4a \qquad -4a$

$8 = 2a - 2$

(Now solve $8 = 2a - 2$)

$8c + 1 = 9c - 4$ $\qquad$ $6d - 3 = 2d + 7$

$10e - 6 = 4e + 9$ $\qquad$ $3f - 4 = 6f - 12$

2. Solve these equations. Do your working out *on paper*.

$4g + 1 = 3g + 8$ $\qquad$ $5h - 5 = 3h + 2$ $\qquad$ $7j - 1 = 4j + 6$

$6k + 4 = 20 - 2k$ $\qquad$ $4n - 8 = 10 - 5n$ $\qquad$ $2p + 4 = 34 - 6p$

Remember to check all solutions by **substituting.**

Teacher's tips

Balance the equation to get all the same letters on the same side. Be careful – if there is more than one letter in an equation (e.g. $2e = 4 - b$) the solution will be the relationship between the letters.

Formulae

Practice

- Algebra is used for many different purposes in real life. One of the most important is being able to **substitute** values into a **formula**.

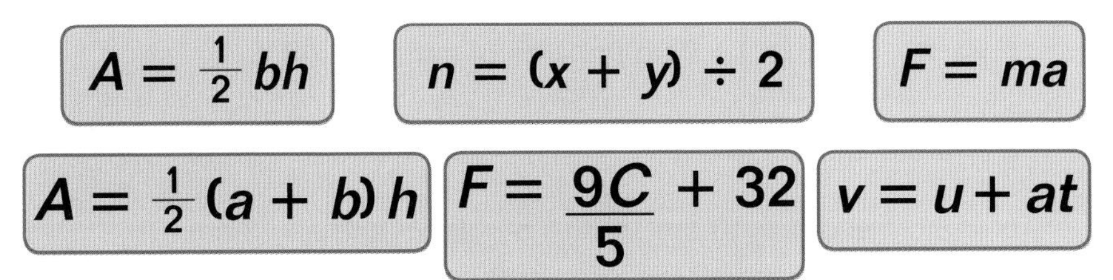

- A formula shows the relationship between two or more things. **Formulae** are like **equations**: they have an equals sign. The first formula above tells us the relationship between the **area** of a triangle (A) and its **base** (b) and **height** (h).

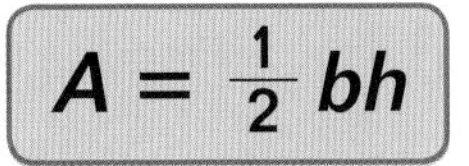

If the base and height are known, the area can be worked out.

- These are worked out by substituting.

Here, it is said that A is the **subject of the formula**. It is alone on one side of the equals sign.

Find the area of a triangle where $b = 4$ cm and $h = 9$ cm.

$$A = \frac{1}{2}bh$$

$A = \frac{1}{2} \times 4 \times 9 = $ **18 cm²**

- The second formula above shows how to find a number (n) that is halfway between two other numbers (x and y). n is the subject of the formula.

It is possible to make any letter in a formula the subject of the formula. The same balancing rules as before are used. (See pages 29 and 30.)

Find the number that is halfway between 28 and 54.

$$n = (x + y) \div 2$$

$n = (28 + 54) \div 2 = $ **41**

- Making x the subject of the formula:

$$n = (x + y) \div 2$$

Let us get rid of the $\div$ **2** on the right by multiplying both sides by 2.

To get rid of the **+ y** on the right, subtract y from both sides.

$\times 2$ $\quad\quad\quad\quad$ $\times 2$
$2n = x + y$
$-y$ $\quad\quad$ $-y$
$2n - y = x$

This gives **$2n - y = x$** or **$x = 2n - y$**

Word wise

The plural of formula is formulae.

Remember this

Remember that the multiplication sign is not usually used in algebra, the numbers or letters are just written next to each other.

$F = m \times a$ is the same as

$F = ma$.

This formula is used in science to show the relationship between force, mass and acceleration.

Why change the subject?

Look at the formula for the area of a triangle:

$A = bh$

Now, suppose you are given the **area** and the **base**, could you work out the **height**? To do so, you would need to change the **subject of the formula** to get the formula:

$h = 2A \div b$

Then it is easy.

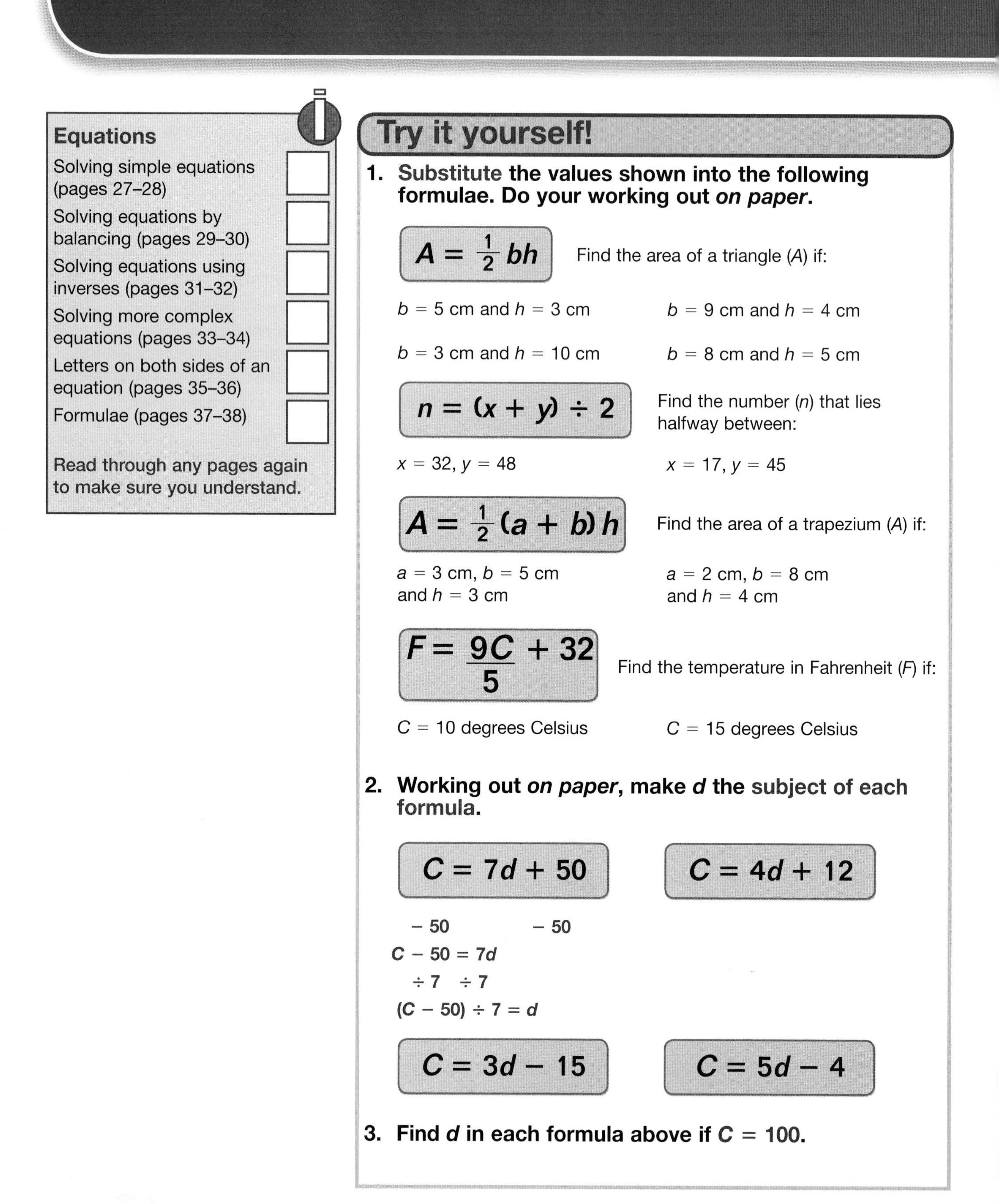

Equations

- Solving simple equations (pages 27–28) ☐
- Solving equations by balancing (pages 29–30) ☐
- Solving equations using inverses (pages 31–32) ☐
- Solving more complex equations (pages 33–34) ☐
- Letters on both sides of an equation (pages 35–36) ☐
- Formulae (pages 37–38) ☐

Read through any pages again to make sure you understand.

Try it yourself!

1. Substitute the values shown into the following formulae. Do your working out *on paper*.

$$A = \frac{1}{2}bh$$

Find the area of a triangle (A) if:

$b = 5$ cm and $h = 3$ cm

$b = 9$ cm and $h = 4$ cm

$b = 3$ cm and $h = 10$ cm

$b = 8$ cm and $h = 5$ cm

$$n = (x + y) \div 2$$

Find the number (n) that lies halfway between:

$x = 32, y = 48$

$x = 17, y = 45$

$$A = \frac{1}{2}(a + b)h$$

Find the area of a trapezium (A) if:

$a = 3$ cm, $b = 5$ cm and $h = 3$ cm

$a = 2$ cm, $b = 8$ cm and $h = 4$ cm

$$F = \frac{9C}{5} + 32$$

Find the temperature in Fahrenheit (F) if:

$C = 10$ degrees Celsius

$C = 15$ degrees Celsius

2. Working out *on paper*, make d the subject of each formula.

$$C = 7d + 50$$

$$C = 4d + 12$$

$-50 \quad -50$

$C - 50 = 7d$

$\div 7 \quad \div 7$

$(C - 50) \div 7 = d$

$$C = 3d - 15$$

$$C = 5d - 4$$

3. Find d in each formula above if $C = 100$.

Teacher's tips

The core formula remains constant; we substitute the letters for the numbers that they represent (this time) in order to solve it for this set of numbers, or rearrange it to focus on the letter of most interest (this time).

Activity cards

Percentage cards

20%	80%	5%	0%	41%	71%	99%
10%	70%	3%	15%	39%	67%	95%
75%	60%	2%	12%	32%	65%	100%
25%	40%	1%	11%	28%	53%	85%
50%	30%	90%	7%	23%	45%	72%

Activity cards

Activity cards

Number cards

200	140	180	660	360
80	760	580	420	320
40	800	340	480	280
120	160	260	220	240

Activity cards

Activity cards

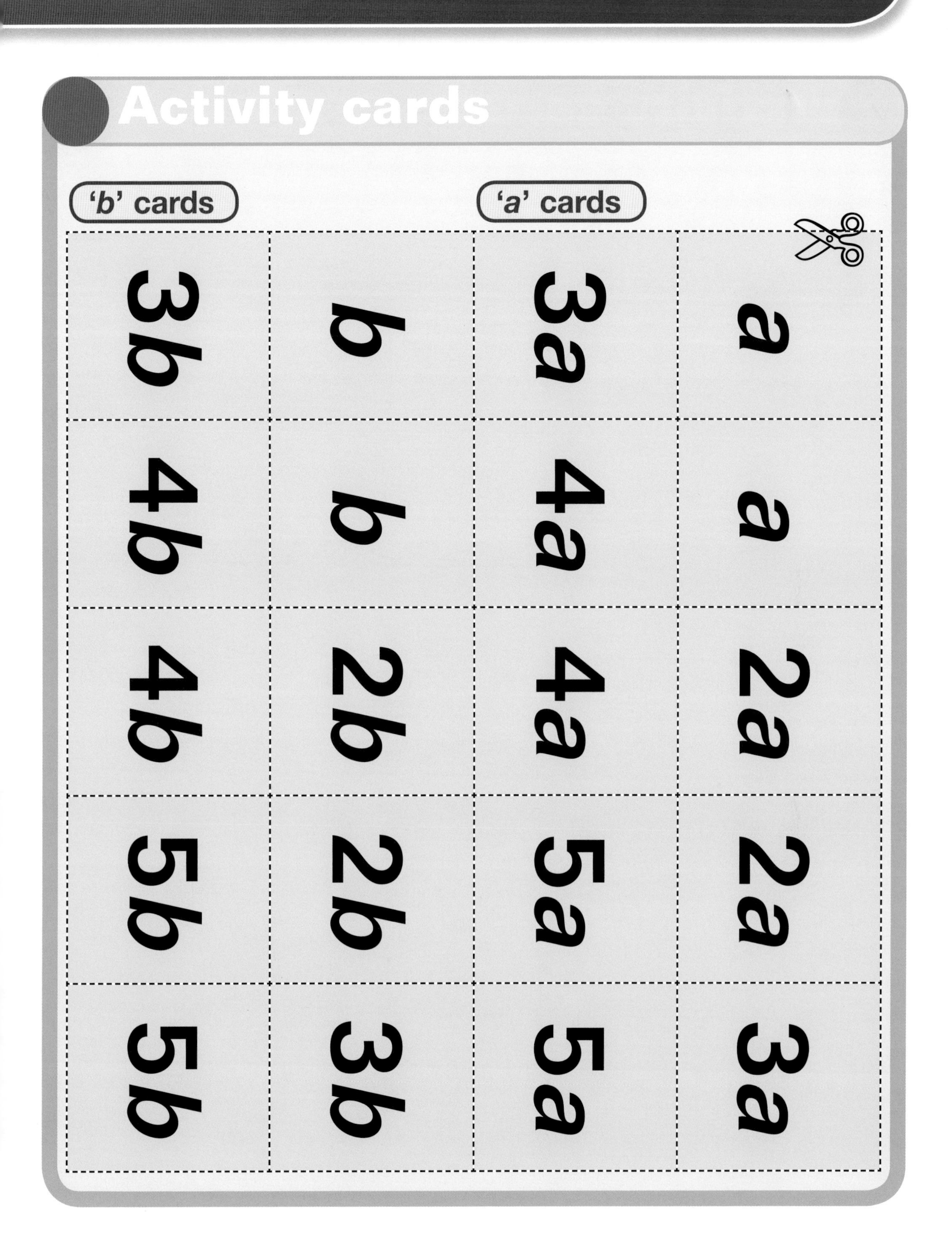

Activity cards

Activity cards

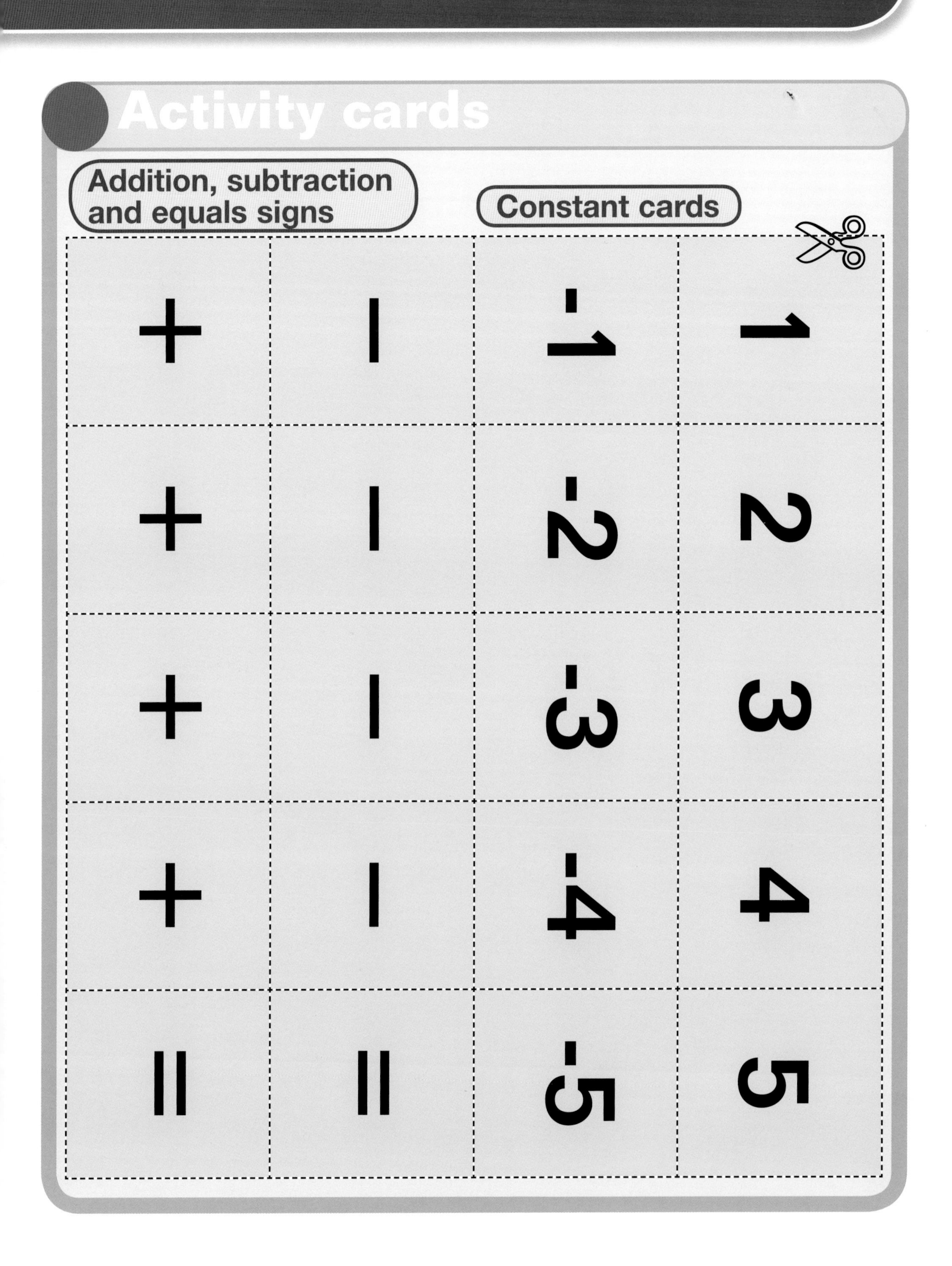

Activity cards

Answers

ESTIMATING PERCENTAGES (PAGE 4)

These are all estimates. Your answers could be up to 10% different from these answers.

1. About 50% About 95% About 10%
   About 75% About 5%
2. About 75% About 50% About 20%
   About 35% About 80%
3. About 80% About 90% About 50%
   About 10% About 10%
   About 60% About 70% About 40%
   About 50% About 3%

OUT OF 100 (PAGE 5)

$\frac{50}{100} = \frac{1}{2}$ $\frac{10}{100} = \frac{1}{10}$ $\frac{25}{100} = \frac{1}{4}$

$\frac{75}{100} = \frac{3}{4}$ $\frac{20}{100} = \frac{1}{5}$

OUT OF 100 (PAGE 6)

1. About 80% About 15% About 35%
   About 95%
2. $\frac{13}{100}$ $\frac{27}{100}$ $\frac{81}{100}$ $\frac{99}{100}$ $\frac{39}{100}$ $\frac{11}{100}$ $\frac{2}{100}$ $\frac{47}{100}$
3. 55 ÷ 100 38 ÷ 100 84 ÷ 100
   13 ÷ 100 6 ÷ 100 10 ÷ 100
4. $\frac{20}{100} = \frac{1}{5}$ $\frac{10}{100} = \frac{1}{10}$ $\frac{75}{100} = \frac{3}{4}$
   $\frac{5}{100} = \frac{1}{20}$ $\frac{80}{100} = \frac{4}{5}$ $\frac{2}{100} = \frac{1}{50}$

PERCENTAGES, FRACTIONS AND DECIMALS (PAGE 8)

1. 0.25 0.32 0.67
   0.21 0.86 0.05
   0.03 0.2 (or 0.20) 0.5 (or 0.50)
   0.8 (or 0.80)
2. 0.55 0.35 0.74
   0.18 0.07 0.32
   0.1 (or 0.10) 0.99 1 (or 1.0 or 1.00)
   0.01 0.4 (or 0.40) 0.33
3. 30% $\frac{30}{100} = \frac{3}{10}$ 0.3 90% $\frac{90}{100} = \frac{9}{10}$ 0.9

   2% $\frac{2}{100} = \frac{1}{50}$ 0.02 15% $\frac{15}{100} = \frac{3}{20}$ 0.15

   8% $\frac{8}{100} = \frac{2}{25}$ 0.08

CALCULATING PERCENTAGES IN YOUR HEAD (PAGE 10)

1. £300 £60 £340 36kg 24kg 420kg
   £150 £30 £170 18kg 12kg 210kg
   £450 £90 £510 54kg 36kg 630kg
2. £40 £55 £66 35kg 45kg 145kg
   12ml 105ml 115ml 36m 27m 92m
3. £42 £6000 £39

CALCULATING OTHER PERCENTAGES (PAGE 12)

1. £60 £12 £68 7.2kg 4.8kg 8.4kg
   £120 £24 £136 14.4kg 9.6kg 16.8kg
2. £18 £24 £72 28kg 99kg 7kg
   56ml 48ml 240ml 126m 77 km 55.2m
3. £48 £3600 117 ounces

CALCULATING PERCENTAGES WITH A CALCULATOR (PAGE 14)

1. £19.20 £30.72 £85.36 29.4kg
   20.16kg 16.1kg 14.79ml 36.25ml
   250.1ml 143.55m 84.96m 66.24m
2. £20.16 £4200 111.8 ounces 36.18mph
   £12.78 £4.20

WRITING SOMETHING AS A PERCENTAGE (PAGE 16)

1. 80% 85% 92.31% 20%
   72.5% 93.33% 64.29% 61.54%
2. 84% 91.43% 91.25% 82.5%
   87.5% 90% Richard
3. 40% 60%

PROBLEMS, PROBLEMS (PAGE 18)

1. 35g 6.4% 17.78% 3 biscuits
   63ml £10.15
2. Class 1W has 54 boys, Class 2G has 52 boys
   Megan has 77.69%, Rachel has 85.45%, Rachel has higher percentage.

PERCENTAGE INCREASES AND DECREASES (PAGE 20)

These are estimates. Your answers might be up to 10% different.

1. 50% 100% 25% 200%
2. 25% 68% 90% 100%

PERCENTAGE INCREASES (PAGE 21)

6392 £56.40

PERCENTAGE INCREASES (PAGE 22)

1. £99.20 £41 £87.36 £105.09
   £196.98 £394.44
2. 68.44mph 64.96kg 2106 £79.90

PERCENTAGE DECREASES (PAGE 23)

3065 £9.80

PERCENTAGE DECREASES (PAGE 24)

1. £60.80 £9 £8.64 £80.91
   £71.02 £61.56
2. 47.56mph 51.04kg 1014 £21 840

INCREASING AND DECREASING MORE THAN ONCE (PAGE 26)

1. £5000 increased by 35% followed by further increase of 35% = £9112.50. More by £612.50
   £5000 increased by 70% = £8500

   £4000 decreased by 30% followed by further decrease of 30% = £1960. More by £360
   £4000 decreased by 60% = £1600

Answers

£9000 decreased by 15% followed by further decrease of 15% = £6502.50. More by £202.50
£9000 decreased by 30% = £6300

SOLVING SIMPLE EQUATIONS (PAGE 28)

1. $a = 3$
   $b = 8$
   $c = 8$
   $d = 3$
   $e = 2$
   $f = 18$
   $g = 10$
   $h = 5$
   $j = 2$
   $k = 4$
   $m = 6$
   $n = 7$
2. $n + 6 = 23, n = 17$
   $n - 11 = 44, n = 55$
   $27 - n = 18, n = 9$
   $5n = 40, n = 8$
3. $p = 20$
   $q = 20$
   $r = 9$
   $s = 5$
   $t = 40$
   $u = 48$

SOLVING EQUATIONS BY BALANCING (PAGE 30)

1. $b = 10$
   $c = 8$
   $d = 7$
   $e = 6$
2. $f = 11$
   $g = 4$
   $h = 5$
   $k = 3$

SOLVING EQUATIONS USING INVERSES (PAGE 32)

1. $b = 10$
   $c = 8$
   $d = 7$
2. $e = 5$
   $f = 8$
   $g = 5$
   $h = 5$
   $j = 9$
   $k = 11$
   $m = 6$
   $n = 7$
   $p = 8$

SOLVING MORE COMPLEX EQUATIONS (PAGE 34)

1. $5a + 10 = 30; a = 4$
   $3b + 12 = 15; b = 1$
   $2c - 10 = 6; c = 8$
   $4h - 12 = 28; h = 10$
   $9j + 9 = 36; j = 3$
   $6k - 10 = 32; k = 7$
   $10m - 30 = 30; m = 6$
   $32 = 10n + 12; n = 2$
   $15 = 12p - 21; p = 3$
2. $e = 2.5$
   $f = 0.75$
   $g = 1.2$
   $h = 6.5$
   $j = 6.5$
   $k = 4.3$
   $m = 15.67$
   $n = 3.57$
   $p = 5.39$

LETTERS ON BOTH SIDES OF AN EQUATION (PAGE 36)

1. $a = 5$
   $b = 5$
   $c = 5$
   $d = 2.5$
   $e = 2.5$
   $f = 2.67$
2. $g = 7$
   $h = 3.5$
   $j = 2.33$
   $k = 2$
   $n = 2$
   $p = 3.75$

FORMULAE (PAGE 38)

1. 7.5 cm^2 18 cm^2 15 cm^2 20 cm^2
   40 31 12 cm^2 20 cm^2
   50 °F 59 °F
2. $(C - 50) \div 7 = d$
   $(C - 12) \div 4 = d$
   $(C + 15) \div 3 = d$
   $(C + 4) \div 5 = d$
3. $d = 7.14$
   $d = 22$
   $d = 38.33$
   $d = 20.8$